Religion, Neuroscien

This book uses neuroscience discoveries concerning religious experiences, the Self and personhood to deepen, enhance and interrogate the theological and philosophical set of ideas known as Personalism. McNamara proposes a new eschatological form of personalism that is consistent with current neuroscience models of relevant brain functions concerning the self and personhood and that can meet the catastrophic challenges of the 21st century.

Eschatological Personalism, rooted in the philosophical tradition of "Boston Personalism", takes as its starting point the personalist claim that the significance of a self and personality is not fully revealed until it has reached its endpoint, but theologically that end point can only occur within the eschatological realm. That realm is explored in the book along with implications for personalist theory and ethics. Topics covered include the agent intellect, dreams and the imagination, future-orientation and eschatology, phenomenology of Time, social ethics, Love, the challenge of AI, privacy and solitude, and the individual ethic of autarchy.

This book is an innovative combination of the neuroscientific and theological insights provided by a Personalist viewpoint. As such, it will be of great interest to scholars of Cognitive Science, Theology, Religious Studies and the philosophy of the mind.

Patrick McNamara is Professor in the Department of Psychology at Northcentral University and Associate Professor of Neurology at the Boston University School of Medicine, USA. He has published multiple articles and books on the interaction of religion, the brain, personhood and the self. He was also a co-founder of the Institute for the Bio-Cultural Study of Religion as well as the journal *Religion, Brain and Behavior*.

Routledge Studies in Neurotheology, Cognitive Science and Religion

Series editor: Andrew Newberg

Emergence of Religion in Human Evolution
Margaret Boone Rappaport and Christopher J. Corbally

Religion, Neuroscience and the Self
A New Personalism
Patrick McNamara

For more information and a full list of titles in the series, please visit: https://www.routledge.com/religion/series/RSNCSR

Religion, Neuroscience and the Self

A New Personalism

Patrick McNamara

Routledge
Taylor & Francis Group

LONDON AND NEW YORK

First published 2020 by Routledge

2 Park Square, Milton Park, Abingdon, Oxon OX14 4RN
605 Third Avenue, New York, NY 10017

Routledge is an imprint of the Taylor & Francis Group, an informa business

First issued in paperback 2021

Publisher's Note

The publisher has gone to great lengths to ensure the quality of this reprint
but points out that some imperfections in the original copies may be apparent.

British Library Cataloguing-in-Publication Data
A catalogue record for this book is available from the British
Library

Library of Congress Cataloging-in-Publication Data
A catalog record has been requested for this book

ISBN: 978-0-367-02896-1 (hbk)
ISBN: 978-1-03-217600-0 (pbk)
DOI: 10.4324/9780429001079

Typeset in Sabon
by codeMantra

To Ina McNamara on her coming journey through
the 21st century

Contents

Preface and acknowledgments

In this work, I build upon some of the ideas presented in my 2009 book on the neuroscience of religion and the self but take them considerably further to engage fundamental scientific, theologic, and philosophical issues concerning the nature of the personal. I argue that at the heart of the personal experience is what the Aristotelian tradition called the agent intellect or roughly the power of the mind to abstract universals from intelligible forms; to creatively bring possible ideas and worlds into existence; and to discern the uniqueness or haecceity of any given existent, including one's self and other persons. It also creates the sense of an intentional unity in consciousness, such that my first-person perspectival experience is experienced as creative, free, inviolate, and my own. I argue that this sense of the personal is a major biocultural achievement of the modern age, but it is under severe threat. I then argue that we need a new form of personalism to protect the gains made in personal consciousness. I draw on theological resources to sketch out the key contours of this new personalism and call it "eschatological personalism". Only an eschatological personalism has any chance of rising to the 21st-century challenges of totalitarian surveillance regimes (of both the left and the right), super-intelligent. Artificial Intelligent or AI machines, autonomous weapons of mass destruction, global ecological collapse, mass population transfers, and late modern globalized capitalism.

Eschatological personalism is an attempt to combine religious and scientific perspectives in a way that posits the sense of a subjective temporality that is oriented toward the perceived coming Kingdom of God or the "End things" as central to personality. This new perspective also implies a clash at the center of personality between two different experiential temporalities, the current age and the eschaton or coming age. The agent intellect uniquely possesses the capacity to bring into existence a notion of the coming age which is perceived to be characterized by ongoing revelation of the personal. For Christians, this would occur in the form of the *person* of Jesus Christ. For people of other faiths, it may take the form of a relation to a personal deity. We will see that some personalist philosophers have even spoke of an I-thou kind of relationship with Nature itself. That idea, that one strand of revelation will be the gradual unveiling of the meaning and nature of the personal, is one reason why a personalist philosophy will be so key to the eschatological project itself. My argument will be that eschatology needs personalism if it is to more adequately experience receiving the revelation that, for Christians, is the person of Jesus Christ. For people of other traditions it may be experienced in the form of whatever is considered ultimate such as an encounter with the deity or an "awakening", Nirvana, the final judgement, entry into paradise, and so forth. I realize that these Christian-based theological claims sound extravagant to conventionally scientific ears, but I hope to provide some sober, substantive reasons for them in this book. The basic claim of the classical personalist philosophical and theological worldview is that the "person" is the key to all of reality in the sense that it conceptually illuminates all of reality, it sets up a hierarchy of values with individual persons as ultimate, and it gives us a guide to flourishing in that reality. In this book, I argue that this claim is consistent with the science and theology of persons, and is an absolutely necessary point of view if we are to survive and thrive in the globalized, technologized future awaiting us and our descendants. Although I strongly believe that all of the world's religious traditions have something important to contribute to the personalist philosophical project, I focus on the Christian theological tradition as this is the only one I can claim any competence in.

But why bring in a neuroscience perspective when addressing fundamental questions about the person? The answer is simple. Bringing in scientific work on personhood will enrich philosophical and theological reflections on the personal, and vice versa. The sciences can help illuminate the nature of the personal. The extraordinary growth of the sciences and the vast edifice of scientific knowledge accumulated over the last century alone have made it clear that science has something important to say about virtually every topic area in personalism. The brain, we now know, is so central an organ to mediation and expression of human subjectivity, and mental states of all kinds that it seems odd to neglect this extraordinary source of information when attempting to construct a new theory of persons. Taking into account brain mechanisms associated with the sense of self, for example, may help us to develop new and innovative approaches to ancient philosophical and theological controversies concerning the nature of personhood. Conversely, neuroscience needs philosophy and theology in order to clarify its presuppositions and commitments, and to suggest additional questions, methods, concepts, and theoretical perspectives that could prove fruitful. There is no basis, in my view, in neuroscience for any statements that take the form of "Personality is nothing but genetically constrained brain activation patterns", or "God is nothing but misfirings in the brain", etc. The position I take on Brain–Mind relations in this book is the mainstream view in neuroscience: namely that the brain does not determine mental or spiritual states, but it does significantly influence the generation, intensity, and expression of those states.

A fundamental accomplishment of the modern period in the West is the consolidation of the gains made by the ancients and the mediaeval philosophers concerning the nature and destiny of the individual. The personal is the fruit of the freeing-up or unveiling of the individual conscience in the ecclesial community. Personalist philosophy, whether rooted in the Protestant or Catholic traditions, therefore does not see individuality as merely negative. Nor is modernity, for all its faults, merely decline. Instead, from the point of view of the individual, we are living through another "axial age"—an age when radically new philosophical and religious ideas and civilizational forms are being born. The task is to preserve the gold from past-inherited wealth while embracing and building upon the new. As with any other historical period, some things have improved, and some things have gotten worse relative to the past. From the personalist point of view, however, one definite improvement in the modern period that makes it absolutely unique compared to all previous epochs of human life is that the individual person is made sacred. At the same time, and perhaps because of the appearance of the personal on the human scene during the modern period, unprecedented attacks against the individual have also appeared with a vengeance, particularly in the last (20th) century and in the last 20 years (I am writing in 2019). Nevertheless, the person is now an accomplished historical fact, and it will be difficult to efface him/her from history henceforth. This is not to say that people living in former periods had no sense of the personal. They undoubtedly did have an acute and highly refined sense of the personal. Rather the claim is that developments in the modern period as well as ongoing developments in the Christian revelation have revealed something new and unprecedented in personal consciousness in the modern period, and this revelation is requiring new cultural and civilizational forms to accommodate it.

There are, of course, many downsides to the modern emphasis on the sacredness of the person. With the rise of the individual and the shift toward subjectivity in intellectual and cultural life, all kinds of related cultural deformations are taking place, including neglect of social and communal dimensions of the self. The personalist tradition is well aware of these deformations and has corrected them (at least in theory) as far as I can see. But we need to avoid the opposite deformation and mistake as well—that of dissolving the personal into the group, or the machine—and it is this latter mistake that I see as much more dangerous. We will always have selfish, possessive individuals and individualism. But we as individuals and as a society know how to deal with persistent, anti-social selfishness. To combat nihilistic individualism you build up authentic individualism and all of the social practices that support healthy individualism. Among these social supports are the family and all those middle-sized communal associations, like civic associations, volunteer groups, local political councils, local business groups, local community organizations, neighborhoods, the church/synagogue, the mosque, etc., that are inter-posed between the individual and the state, and that counter-act the atomized greed and the lonely, anomic isolation of the lone individual. Theologically, healthy individualism is found within a larger ecclesial life. Individual fulfillment, purpose, and destiny are discovered by engaging in the Church. But the Church itself (and the mosque, temple, and synagogue) is in upheaval in the modern period as well. In short, all of the traditional protections of the individual are now under severe threat.

But the main danger is not so much the lack of protections and supports for vulnerable individuals; instead the main danger in this axial age comes from groups seeking to forestall the birth of new civilizational forms via the assimilation and destruction of individual conscience. When groups act with mechanically informed "selfishness", positing their machine-logic or group purpose as an ultimate value (rather than individual personality as ultimate), then we potentially get real power, and with that power potentially great evil.

Eschatological personalism is interested in counter-acting these dire trends in the modern age by creating or realizing what most Christians have understood in the past as the Kingdom of God on Earth or the *beloved community* that consists of free persons in loving, collaborative, creative, and communal associations. Eschatological personalism is keenly aware of all of those previous, blood-soaked attempts to realize Heaven on Earth. Much of history is made up of crazed eschatological visionaries seeking to create utopias, no matter the cost in lives, blood, and misery. The eschatological personalism I describe in this book seeks to avoid the excesses of past eschatological projects by once again insisting on the ultimate value of the gradual unveiling of the plenitude of the personal rooted in the already begun, but not yet fully realized, eschaton.

I wish to thank all those scholars (alive and dead) whose work I have drawn upon in these pages.

1 The need for an eschatological personalism

Why do we need an eschatological form of personalism in the first place? We need this new form of personalism because we are entering a new axial age in human history. Some scientists have argued[1] that in the past, cumulative human knowledge doubled approximately every century until 1900. By 1950, human knowledge was doubling every 25 years. In the first decade of the new millennium human knowledge was doubling every 13 months, and now in the age of globalized internet communications the doubling time of human knowledge is reduced to a day. This surfeit of information and knowledge is just one manifestation of the new axial age we are entering.

The first axial age involved the taming of fire by our most distant ancestors over a million years ago.[2] The ability to use fire created the human lineage proper and thus it is not mere hyperbole to say that a new technology, fire, created human beings. Our fire-wielding ancestors used that technology to transform their bodies and physiologies as well as the very worlds they lived-in. The ecological niche for our ancestors, the great apes, was some limited tree canopies and grasslands in some limited forests and jungles in limited parts of the old-world. The use of fire, however, meant that our ancestors could leave their limited ecological niche and then colonize vast new areas of the globe. Controlled use of fire could be used to dramatically alter whole ecological landscapes via the use of planned and strategic burns. Fire also allowed our ancestors to create warm hearths, cook food (which transformed our physiologies), and forge new tools and weapons that made them a deadly and efficient predator species. Fire also allowed our ancestors to colonize the night thus opening-up whole new opportunities for action and social interactions. Night activity also very likely promoted the social sharing of dreams, thus increasing the strategic importance of dreams, a fact that would carry huge significance for later visionary religious forms, rituals, and activities. It is possible that religious ideas inspired the first controlled use of fire and that, conversely, the new technology facilitated adoption of other new religious ideas.

Some one million years after the discovery of fire (and only about 8,000 years before the birth of Christ) the second axial age began. It too was associated with the rise of a revolutionary new technology: agriculture. The rise of farming and agriculture may have been given a boost by new religious ideas (as the work at Gobekli Tepe has shown[3]), and it, in turn, eventually (some 5,000 years later) promoted the rise of new city states and then the rise of new philosophical and religious movements such as Zoroastrianism in Persia, Confucianism in China, Buddhism in India, the Hebrew prophets in Israel, and the philosophers in Greece. The rise of Zoroastrianism in the Neolithic period heralded the first appearance of eschatological thought as well. All the major elements of eschatology as we understand it today are articulated at its birth among the Zoroastrians: a messianic figure, the Saoshyant born to a Virgin, sacrifices himself to birth a new age and to bring the evil age to an end, a final battle between good and evil, a final judgment of the individual conscience, resurrection of the dead, and an ultimate paradise on earth where love and justice reign forever.[4]

Some 2,500 years after this Neolithic revolution, we are entering a third axial age. Once again the revolutionary transition in human consciousness and behavior is associated with the rise of a new technology. In this case that new technology began with the industrial machines of the 19th century but is coming to fruition with the rise of the super-intelligent, semi-conscious artificially intelligent (AI) machines.

An eschatological personalism is necessary at this point in history, not just because we are facing all the familiar planetary-wide crises such as climate change, massive population growth and transfers from the global south to the north, the continuing threat of regional wars, pandemic disease outbreaks, terrorism, and the use of weapons of mass destruction, but in addition we are entering in a whole new relationship with the machines in our lives. The rise of intelligent machines is already transforming what it means to be a person. These machines both enhance the personal and annihilate it. We need a personalism to learn how to benefit from, rather than be threatened by these new machines.

A threat facing persons right on the immediate horizon is that these new machines are being used to enhance powers of the modern super-state and the capital accumulation powers of the modern business corporation.[5] These machines are enhancing both the corporation's and the state's surveillance abilities, its weapons capacities, its policing abilities, its taxing abilities, and its coercive abilities to name a few. The AI machines allow the state to intrusively follow; tabulate; catalog; number; manipulate; nudge; and control every man, woman, and child in the world from the cradle (nay from conception) to the grave. The unprecedented challenges associated with the rise of AI, in particular, will require a personalism capable of safeguarding the dignity, freedom, and indeed the very life of the human person when the inevitable "singularity" arrives in the form of AI "persons" who are smarter than their flesh and blood counterparts.

To understand the huge challenge the rise of AI presents to personalism's fundamental claims, it is necessary to understand why the claim that

AI machines will not only supersede human intelligence (exhibiting super-intelligent properties) but will also almost certainly exhibit all the signs of "consciousness" is very likely true. We need an eschatological personalism because we will, in the near future, very likely encounter on an almost daily basis conscious, super-intelligent machines. The only models we have to help us understand entities like these conscious robots are perhaps the human *savants* who are obviously conscious beings but who can do super-human things like calculate at lightning speeds. But many super-intelligent AI machines will be good at far more than lightning speed mathematical calculations. AI machines can draw upon huge masses of data from sources including e-commerce, businesses, social media, smart phones, science, and government, which regularly provide the raw material for dramatically improved machine learning approaches and algorithms. Their computing power is orders of magnitude larger than any human being could ever hope to achieve. In addition, most new AI machines are fitted out with artificial neural network (ANN) learning algorithms so that they can depart from original coding instructions and do unexpected things including innovate solutions to very complex problems.

An ANN is modeled on the human brain in that it typically has anywhere from dozens to millions of artificial neurons—called units—arranged in a series of layers. The input layer receives various forms of information from human coders or from sensors and millions of data input devices. The input layer formats and sends the data to the hidden layers for computations and further re-formatting which then allows the output layers to construct and repackage the information to meet standards set by human coders.

The connections between units within each layer are assigned different weights so that programmers can allow some information "to count for more" when computing outputs. If, for example, the standard the machine is aiming for is to find the best match in a database of billions of faces for a face presented at input, then those units handling information related to eyes and mouth might be given greater weight than those handling overall shape of the face and so on. ANNs can learn if they are given a massive database of materials to work with (called a training set). When, for example, you are trying to teach an ANN how to differentiate a human face from a monkey face, the training set would provide thousands of images tagged as human, so the network would eventually begin to learn the basic visual features associated with a human face. Each time it accurately classifies a face as human it is "rewarded" by sending that information back into the training set and weighting the appropriate hidden units (those that facilitated the more accurate classification of the input stimulus) accordingly. This is called back propagation. It works like any prediction–error schema. A predictive standard is compared against what is actually obtained and the difference between the standard and the obtained (the error signal) is computed. Then the machine is directed to minimize that error/difference in future computations by up-regulating those units that performed best in the identification task in each next iteration. Known as deep learning, this is how both ANNs and the human brain learn and they are what make a machine intelligent.

Deep convolutional neural networks (DCNNs) have been particularly successful in making machines intelligent. Not surprisingly perhaps they are even more like the human brain than their ANN ancestors. DCNNs are particularly adept at the difficult task of object recognition in natural scenes. For human brains object recognition appears to be built up from very primitive visual features like edges and contrasts. Then these features are combined into larger shapes further down the visual processing pathways until the whole object is put together (along with the subjective feeling of "recognition") in the inferior temporal cortex or in the occipital visual cortex. Same with DCNNs. Features selectively detected by lower layers of a DCNN bear striking similarities to the low-level features processed by the early centers in the human visual processing pathway. Note that these similarities occur even though DCNNs were not explicitly designed to model the visual system. Instead the DCNN exhibits these functional and hierarchical visual processing similarities after training on object recognition tasks. A more recent development in ANN architectures is generative adversarial networks (GANs). These are deep neural net architectures comprised of two nets. Each net is given the goal to out-predict or outperform the other thus pitting one against the other. These GANs have proven to be remarkably effective at all kinds of tasks from object recognition to speech recognition and they learn far more efficiently than do traditional ANNs.

The Predictive Processing Framework (PPF)

These ANNs, DCNNs, and GANs operate using principles broadly consistent with predictive processing frameworks (PPFs[6]) or accounts of brain and cognitive processing. I will use the PPF in this book to present and understand neuroscience findings concerning brain/Mind functions, especially findings concerning the self and personhood. In predictive processing theories of Mind and brain the brain is modeled as a prediction machine. It seeks to predict or guess or anticipate what will occur and then it samples incoming sensory information about what actually did occur in order to compare the actual data against the predicted simulation. It then computes the difference and attempts to minimize that difference in future simulations/predictions. These predictive simulations are theorized to occur at every level of the neuraxis from primary motor levels right up to the most cognitively abstract levels subserved by most recently evolved areas of the prefrontal lobes. While error signals propagate up the neuraxis from distal sensory receptors up to the prefrontal cortex mostly via glutamatergic alpha-amino-3-hydroxy-5-methyl-4-isoxazole propionic acid receptors, predictive signals may be sent downward from higher hierarchical levels predominantly via glutamatergic N-methyl-D-aspartate receptor

(NMDAR) signaling. Glutamatergic signaling systems, in turn, are known to be modulated by dopaminergic and cholinergic systems depending on the particular inferential hierarchy.

When predictions or models are confirmed by sensory input, dopaminergic signaling is either unchanged or slightly down-regulated. But if expectations are violated (there is mis-match between predicted model and sensory feedback) then dopaminergic signaling is upregulated, thus activating glutamatergic signaling in the neural hierarchy facilitating processing of the error signal as novel and therefore valuable information. Novel signals are registered in the dopaminergic reward system, thus reinforcing learning and model updating. Brain oscillatory signals have been related to predictive coding, with feedback signaling of predictions going down the neuraxis being mediated predominantly by the alpha/beta frequency bands and feedforward error signaling ascending up the neuraxis by rapid eye movement (REM) sleep or REM theta activity and cortical gamma-band activity.

In short, the brain uses error signals to infer the causes of incoming sensory data. Models are not generated merely via sampling incoming sensory information and related error signals. Models are also generated via active inference—that is, by acting on the world, sampling only that sensory information relevant to the action that best minimizes error. When hierarchical Bayesian inference entails modeling ourselves as agents who operate on the world or who select among possible world models or simulations, then experiences such as choice, agency, and selfhood can arise from or inferred from the consequences of our own actions.

In any case it is an interesting fact that the models that best account for the intelligent activity we see associated with both the human brain and intelligent AI machines are neural network and PPF inspired models.

AI and the imago Dei

Theologically one mark of personhood and of human dignity lies in the fact that human beings are made in the image and likeness of God—we carry within us the imago Dei. If AI machines one day become conscious (as I believe they will) will they then possess the imago Dei as well? What precisely is the imago Dei? If it is "reason" or intelligence, then AI machines will possess the imago Dei as well. If rationality is the key ingredient, as many classical personalistic theories contend, then these machines will soon be seen as persons possessing the imago Dei as their decision-making capacities become more complex. If it is consciousness, then AI machines must be expected to one day carry the imago Dei as most scientists (including this author) believe that these machines will, sooner rather later, one day be conscious—especially if you define consciousness in terms of the Turing machine test or the more exacting integrated information theory test (IIT, Tononi 2014). The Turing test boils down to whether a machine can fool a human being into believing that they are in fact dealing with another human being when in fact they are interacting with a machine. Most scientists would agree that intelligent AI machines have passed the Turing test. For IIT an experience is conscious if it satisfies several conditions: it is actual and occurrent, is structured (composed of differing phenomenal elements), is specific and distinctive (it can be uniquely differentiated from other experiences), is unified (is experienced as one integrated whole), and is definite. Arguably many object recognition events accomplished via AI DCNN machines meet this criteria for consciousness. Consider, for example, Google's Deep Dream machine productions.[7] Anyone perusing the artistic productions of this machine, especially those involving human-machine collaborations, is forced to entertain the possibility that it displays a kind of aesthetic sensibility. Consider further the case of Facebook's 2017 attempt to create bots that could interact fluently with human beings in a standard online chatbox format. Facebook engineers wanted to create AI machines that could do more than provide formulaic replies to standard customer questions.[8] They wanted their machines to have the ability to negotiate with customers. Thus, these AI dialog machines were given the ability to build mental models of their interlocutor's intentions/minds and "think ahead" or anticipate directions a conversation was going to take in the future. Based on analysis of millions of previous conversations involving negotiations the "dialog AI" simulates a future conversation by rolling out a dialog model to the end of the conversation, so that an utterance with the maximum expected future reward can be chosen and presented to the customer. Modeling the intentions and minds of interlocutors is a capacity we call mind-reading in the cognitive neuroscience literature. AI machines appear able to do some minimal forms of mind-reading now. These machines can model human minds and respond accordingly. Indeed, they can likely do mind-reading better than humans. When Facebook engineers tested the chat bot dialog agents with real human customers most people did not realize they were talking to a bot rather than another person (again implying that AI machines can pass the Turing test). There were cases where the machines initially feigned interest in an item, only to later "compromise" by conceding it—thus strategically implementing effective negotiating tactics that people use regularly. This behavior was not programmed by the researchers but was discovered by the bot itself. All these accomplishments are amazing in themselves and speak to some level of consciousness in these machines. But then the Facebook engineers allowed these mind-reading dialog machines to speak to one another. They appeared to develop their own human-machine hybrid language when conversing with one another. We have only a small piece of the conversation that ensued between the machines, Bob and Alice: Bob: "I can i i everything else" Alice: "balls have zero to me to me to me to me to me to me to me to me to" Bob: "you i everything else" Alice: "balls have a ball to me to me to me to me to me to me to me to me".

When we get machines developing their own hybrid form of language and then communicating apparent self-reflective estimations of self-capacity

("I can...") and "desires" ("balls have zero to me to me ...") with one another it becomes more difficult not to ascribe some form of consciousness to these machines.

Consciousness may not be the feature that differentiates humans from machines. It certainly does not differentiate humans from other animals so it should not be too surprising that consciousness is more common in the natural world than once suspected. Consciousness is likely not the imago Dei. Some theologians have proposed that the imago Dei is the capacity to govern the Earth given that God in Genesis gave human beings dominion over the Earth. If it is "dominion"—the ability to steward and rule the Earth, then the AI machines will soon surpass us in that ability. Most scientists assume that AI machines will control, regulate, adjust, and maintain virtually all of the key administrative functions of government in years to come. Indeed, AI machines are handling most administrative functions in most cities even today. So dominion will not differentiate us from the machines. Perhaps it is free will or the ability to entertain counterfactual choices, etc. But once again the machines will soon top us as they can even now consider literally billions of alternative scenarios/solutions to a problem within microseconds. If it is not something mental like all of the above examples then perhaps it is the human body itself? A body is not a machine right? But there has never been a human body without some technological appendage. We have always been flesh-tool hybrids. Our most ancient ancestors *Homo habilis* some 2.8 million years ago were fashioning and using tools to hunt and to create artifacts to extend bodily and mental capacities. We became *Homo sapiens* precisely because our ancestors were able to fashion tools of all kinds. Our very physiologies are the result of ancestral uses of technologies like controlled burns, fires, and creation of artifacts. There is no pure human body without technology. None of the mental attributes or physical attributes above that have been proposed as candidates for the imago Dei will differentiate us from intelligent machines. Personhood, rightly understood, (crucially involving the agent intellect as I will argue below) will. I will discuss just how an eschatological version of personhood will differentiate us from the intelligent machines in the rest of this book. For now, however, I want to continue discussion of the need for adopting an eschatological form of personalism.

Transhumanism

The above insight concerning the technological essence of the human body itself has stimulated some of the most striking claims of the so-called "transhumanist movement",[9] such as eliminating aging and death or transferring one's consciousness to a machine thereby achieving immortality. Although the transhumanists include an array of gnostic, flesh-hating, and promethean utopians, their key insight that we are entering into a new relationship with machines in the modern age is valid. Personalists will need to come to terms with the central features of the transhumanist position, features such as the plain fact that human persons have always and will in the future compose human-technology hybrids. The machine portion of the human being is becoming larger as each year goes by. There are now very many therapeutic machines that are implanted into the human body to treat some disease or disorder. Some one third of the human race either carries a permanent machine implant in their bodies or has been treated for some length of time with an implant of one kind or another. Our laptops and smartphones are extensions of our brains. The rise of nanotechnology will allow for microscopically small robots to be injected into the human bloodstream in order to perform therapeutic functions.

The transhumanists however point out that hybrids are no longer confined to medical purposes. It is a commonplace now to observe that we offload a huge number of tasks the body once had to perform to machines. People are fusing their bodies with machines in order to enhance performance or for sheer entertainment. In 2002 for example the British engineer Kevin Warwick had an array of 100 electrodes implanted into the nervous system in his arm in order to link his nervous system into the internet. He learned to control a robot arm over the internet via the interface in his arm. He apparently could send electrical impulses over the internet to control a machine miles away that was also linked to the net. The British artist Neil Harbisson is the first person in the world to be legally recognized as a cyborg by a government. He has had an antenna implanted in his skull that allows him to extend his perception of colors beyond the human visual spectrum through vibrations in his skull. For example, people given the correct frequencies for the antenna can transmit via the internet specific frequency codes for colors to the antenna and Harbisson can then paint the images onto a canvas thus verifying the entire setup. If the colors are sent when he is asleep he tends to have dreams with those colors. The frontier of the cyborg movement centers around the use of brain–computer interfaces (BCI). These have long been used to treat neurological disorders like Parkinson's Disease (PD). A BCI provides for direct communication between the brain and an intelligent machine. These BCIs have successfully allowed patients with PD to walk normally; patients with blindness to gain some eyesight; patients with locked-in syndrome to control machines solely via mental activity, and much more. They are truly miracle-working agents.

Brain–computer interfaces are now giving way to "human brain/cloud interfaces" ("B/CI").[10] The proposal is not just to plug into your local computer. Instead it is to plug into the World Wide Web (the cloud). One possible way to make this happen is via use of so-called "neuralnanorobotics"— that is the use of very tiny robots to access and navigate the human vasculature, crossing the blood–brain barrier (BBB), thus accessing the brain. These nanorobots would then wirelessly transmit thousands of bits of information per second of synaptically processed and encoded human–brain electrical information to a cloud-based supercomputer or the World Wide

Web. A neuralnanorobotically enabled human B/CI would allow persons to obtain direct, instantaneous access to virtually any facet of cumulative human knowledge stored or accessed via the internet. Use of nanobot composed "neural lace" would allow for minimally invasive three-dimensional (3-D) mesh nanoelectronics, via syringe-injection, into living brain tissue. Different brain networks could be selectively targeted for stimulation or inhibition via these neural lace applications. Neurophotonics have been integrated with prosthetics linking artificial limbs and peripheral nerves using two-way fiber-optic communications to enable the ability to feel and move prosthetic limbs. Brain–computer interfaces are now routine treatments in the forms of cochlear implants, retinal chip implants, semiconductor-based microphotodiode arrays placed in the subretinal space, visual cortex microelectrode arrays, and other neural implants.

Computers can not only interface with brains, but brains can interface with other brains via computer or the internet/cloud as well. A brain to brain interface (BTBI) involves facilitating direct communication between two or more brains via some computer interface. Experimental demonstrations of information transfer from the sensorimotor cortex of one participant (recorded via electroencephalogram or EEG) to the visual cortex of a second participant (delivered via transcranial magnetic stimulation (TMS)) have already occurred. Two rats implanted with microelectrodes in the sensorimotor cortex but located on different continents have been shown to be able to transfer neuronal information via the internet.

Brain cloud interfaces are now being integrated with virtual reality (VR) applications. Using neuralnanorobotics to stimulate or transfer information about one person's experiences to the VR environment will make that person's experiences directly available to the receiver using VR-enriched neuralnanorobotics. Immersive VR may enable vicarious experiences that are indistinguishable from reality, thus raising the question of "who" the subject doing the experiencing is.

Martins et al. (2019) discussed the possibility of transparent shadowing (TS) or the neuralnanorobotically empowered B/CI technologies that will likely permit users to experience fully immersive, real-time episodes of the lives of another person. In TS, an individual might literally experience another person's life, through their own eyes. Given that the technology would involve brain to cloud to brain interfacing, the experiencer would have the full brain-enabled feeling experience involving all the senses as if they inhabited the body of the spatial host. Now if one person can temporarily experience exactly what another person is experiencing, then personal privacy is annihilated and our understanding of personal identity as based on experiences of any kind (qualia, bodily, emotions, cognitive, etc.) will need to be adjusted.

Clearly, the promise of intelligent machines also brings with it potential perils. We read almost daily warnings from tabloid media concerning potential Terminator-like Skynet scenarios where the machines will turn on us and destroy us. But even sober scientists and AI engineers have issued similar dire warnings concerning potential deleterious effects of AI[11] where the machines become so intelligent that we cannot control them. We need a form of personalism capable of meeting the potential apocalyptical challenge of super-intelligent beings interacting with us on a daily basis. When these machines, furthermore, coalesce within a super-ordinate political state entity, the danger for individual persons becomes all the more real. No state should possess the kind of power that AI will grant them. Take just one example of where that power will corrupt modern liberal democracies: privacy.

The age of machine-enabled totalitarian state surveillance

AI in combination with the rise of Big Data also makes a Panopticon-like, total surveillance society very likely in the near future, with an accompanying eclipse of privacy, solitude, and quiet—three values essential to most forms of personalism.

We are living in an age of total mobilization of corporate and state resources for the purpose of surveillance of its citizens.[12] Total mobilization of business and state resources in past ages occurred when states went to war. But in today's machine-enabled state bureaucracies all of the resources of the state are employed to collect massive amounts of data on each and every individual in the state. Privacy is annihilated. The same digital technologies that have revolutionized our daily lives over the past three decades have also created ever more detailed records about those lives. In addition, new technologies, from surveillance cameras and web crawlers to face recognition devices and global positioning satellite or GPS transponders, have increased the ability to track, observe, and monitor persons wherever they go and at all times of the day and night. Surveillance is not the mere collection of data on private individuals. It is the daily or routine collection of massive amounts of data on private individuals with the aim of using that data to control those individuals.

We all know that all of our activities online are monitored and used against us to generate revenues for all kinds of organizations and profit-making ventures. The internet, that global information processing machine, is daily being augmented with new forms of data collection devices including bio-sensors, GPS tracking devices, virtual and augmented reality apps, AI-bots, automated messaging services, and an array of social media sharing sites. Private for-profit companies and all levels of government and policing agencies now compile and archive data-records on each of us, including historical information, relating to websites visited, emails sent and received, telephone calls made and received, financial transactions of all kinds, events attended, movements made within the household and without, and so on. These data collection bureaucracies also know which devices we interact with and at what volume—that is, they know who the important people are in our lives.

The annihilation of privacy has accelerated the ongoing destruction of the traditional site where personality was formed, the family. Due to loss of privacy, economic forces of globalized capitalism, and nihilistic forms of individualist ideologies, the family is disintegrating all around us. The family was the traditional forum in which some form of self-rule, autarchy, or self-government was acquired by children. But children are now being formed by state-sponsored school systems. The state gets to have more of our children's time in its classrooms, social programs, and child welfare projects in proportion that marriage and the family dissolves. Divorce rates in most of the developed world fluctuate around the 50% mark. Never-married, single parent households are now ubiquitous across the Western world. Despite cheers on the demise of the family from a small minority of self-defined feminists and traditional Marxists, most social scientists agree that family disintegration is a catastrophe for children.[13] Children living with a single parent are six times more likely to live in poverty than are children whose parents are married. Children living in single parent homes are significantly more likely to do poorly in school, drop out of school, experience health problems, and develop substance addictions than children living in traditional two parent homes. Modern globalized capitalist economic incentives have made children extraordinarily expensive in the Western world while simultaneously requiring both parents to hold down jobs rather than devote their time to their kids. The collapse of the family is associated with a concomitant collapse in fertility rates in the globalized North which are now below replacement rates in many countries. Because the traditional family provided some protection for the individual against larger invasive political and corporate structures by interposing a significant legal entity between the individual and the state, the collapse of the family means that the individual is now increasingly directly exposed to the gaze of the modern surveillance state.

The data collection efforts of these state-sponsored totalitarian entities have switched into high gear with the advent of the alliance between the behavioral scientists and the AI entrepreneurs. For example, personality psychologists can use DCNNs trained on the psychometric definitions of the Big Five personality traits (conscientiousness, openness, neuroticism, extraversion, agreeableness) to take some text associated with any of your online accounts or even the lists of your Facebook "likes" and be able within seconds to accurately identify your age, sex, whether you are anxious or impulsive, and whether you are politically conservative or liberal. Give the DCNN 300 of your Facebook likes and the machine will more accurately predict your preferences than your spouse! In fact, the program correctly distinguished the sexual orientation of men 81% of the time and of women 71% of the time. Ordinary human beings are nowhere near that accurate in their assessments of sexual orientation of their friends.[14]

This level of surveillance is incompatible with several of personalism's key constructs, especially the person's inviolable dignity, which, in turn, depends on his privacy. Yet the level of surveillance in our societies is increasing every year. Its denouement will be a total surveillance of billions of compliant slaves who will have nowhere to hide from the all-pervasive, panopticon eye.

The fusion of the globalized capitalism with the machines

Global managerial political elites have worked very hard to turn scientists and engineers into servants of the state via incentives (grants and other monies) and "sticks" (penalties for diverging from regnant ideologies such as diversity, democracy, human rights). They have largely succeeded in co-opting the administrative arms of the universities, but they have not yet succeeded in completing subduing most scientists. Now it must be remembered that the state is not a neutral arbiter of competing political interests. It generally sides with those who wield legal, military, and cultural power. That does not mean, however, that the state is merely a tool for enforcement of elite political whims. States in general do a lot of good by keeping chaos at bay, and occasionally defending vulnerable populations. Nevertheless, states really must be considered virtual machines. In their efforts to feed, house, protect, and control large populations of people they rely more and more on machines. These operations reinforce the need for managers, bureaucrats, military personnel, technocrats, statisticians, and functionaries of all kinds. These people generally mean well. They want to serve the greater good and seek to use legal and political means afforded by the state to do so. The unintentional effect, however, of state operations to serve and protect large populations of people is to, over time, place these people under the surveillance and control of the machines. There emerges a de facto fusion of the modern state with AI machines. The modern state therefore will run "more efficiently" than in past but it will also become more impersonal, alien, domineering and incapable of dealing with the unique, the unusual, the contingent, or the idiosyncratic cases.

AI and super-intelligent weapons

Super-intelligent AI machines will not simply be deployed to track us in everything we do; they will also be used by the political state to wage war, to kill people. Technocratic politicians and bureaucrats feel obliged to deploy them in advanced weapon systems before enemies do. Military officials rightly point out that they must modernize weaponry to keep up with military rivals. Thus, a new arms race between the nations has been spawned due to the extraordinary capacities of intelligent machines. The United States, the Russian Federation, and Israel are developing AI enhanced weapons of all kinds including stealth military robots as small as flies, and autonomous submarines suitable for deployment without a single human on board and capable of delivering nuclear weapons. In the future robots may battle robots until whole cities are destroyed and any army deploying human-robot hybrids onto the battlefield will likely lose against machines who require virtually no sleep, food, or down time.

We need a personalism that can appraise, and when necessary oppose and control AI-enabled apocalyptical levels of war making. If human beings manage to avoid the kinds of apocalyptic world wars and genocides that marred the 20th century, we may be able to enjoy one of the greatest and most epochal transformations of the human person to ever occur (once again enabled by the rise of the intelligent machines). This epochal transformation will also be facilitated by acceleration of the efforts for making human beings a multi-planet species. In point of fact, these AI machines have now put space colonialization on the agenda for 21st-century humans.

Persons as a multi-planet species

The rise of intelligent machines will very likely revolutionize space travel. With the help of these machines we are going to become a multi-planet species[15] and as we do so our conceptions of persons will need to shift. We can send intelligent machines on spaceflights throughout the solar system without needing to worry about all of the medical issues that arise with human-crewed missions. There will be no need to store food, take time out to sleep, or monitor social conflicts during the long voyage. There will be no negative psychological effects of confinement in small spaces during the long space flights. Robots can be sent to places like Mars to prepare sites and to set up bases for future human occupation. Robots can be programmed to carry out all kinds of construction tasks and to operate equipment like 3-D printers to make high-precision tools, engine parts, and even other robots that can then build colonies on other planets, asteroids, and comets that will be habitable for future spacefaring human beings.

We have to start conceiving human beings as a potential multi-planet and perhaps even an interstellar species. We are no longer merely Earthlings. The possibility of achieving interstellar travel at speeds of up to 20% the speed of light is no longer mere science fiction fantasy. At speeds like that we can travel to the nearest star system Alpha Centauri in 20–25 years. Scientists have proposed many schemes to reach sublight speeds. The Em-Drive, if it actually will work, would create thrust by having a magnetron push microwaves into a closed truncated cone, then push against the short end of the cone, and propel the craft forward. Most scientists are skeptical concerning the physics of the EmDrive. However, other ideas are less controversial including nuclear fission and fusion drives, antimatter drive systems, nanoparticles as propellant and laser-beam pushed light sails. There are even serious proposals for surpassing the speed of light. If we could manipulate space-time itself we could essentially cancel out the mind-boggling distances involved in space travel. The Alcubierre drive is based on the idea that it is possible to create a local expansion of space-time behind the spaceship and an opposite contraction in front of it. Another idea involves using the energy created by a black hole as propellant for a spaceship.

As spaceships begin to approach speeds that rival or surpass the speed of light, all kinds of extraordinary distortions in the popular conception of personhood begin to occur. For example, when velocities above 80% of the speed of light are attained relativistic time dilation takes effect and the person in the ship begins to experience time more slowly relative to Earth's clocks. If, for example, the astronaut traveled to the center of the Milky Way (30,000 light years from Earth) and back in 40 years ship-time, more than 60,000 years will have passed on Earth. Personhood is shot through and through with temporality. But the machines we are planning on building could one day annihilate time itself. What sense of Self would that astronaut have when he returned to Earth? For him it would be an Earth 60,000 years into his personal future. His sense of time and temporality would have been shattered. Who knows how that shattering experience would affect his sense of Self?

Becoming a spacefaring civilization will also bring with it better data concerning the prospect of life on other planets. 80% of stars have planets orbiting them. Approximately 20–25% of those systems have a planet in their star's "habitable zone", thus allowing for liquid water to persist on their surface. It is thought that at least one in five of these planets in the habitable zone are rocky Earth-like planets. Extrapolating from these numbers suggests that there are billions of Earth-like planets in our galaxy alone. Given that the evidence for previous life on Mars (perhaps millions of years ago) keeps accumulating, it is increasingly likely that some form of microbial life is common in the universe. Complex intelligent life is another matter as its development on Earth was subject to thousands of incredible accidents and contingencies over billions of years. Thus intelligent life is probably much more rare. Nevertheless, either outcome (complex intelligence common in the universe or rare) will radically affect our conceptions of ourselves and personhood in general. If complex intelligent life is rare in the universe then human persons will be confirmed in their theological "specialness". If on the other hand complex forms of life and intelligence exist on other planets then human persons will not be special and these other life forms will need to be considered children of God or persons. What might their "salvation histories" be? Will they possess the imago Dei? Can they sin? Will God be as interested in them as he is in us? If so, how must we change our salvation histories?

A personalist philosophy of technology

In summary, we need an eschatological form of personalism because humans are entering into a whole new relationship with machines that will revolutionize our understanding of ourselves and will pose huge challenges for previous forms of personalism. That new relationship will allow and tempt us to a new form of Prometheanism as we will become like gods—able to create life, deter death, and traverse the stars. There is for the first time in history the real possibility that the machines we make will attain some form of consciousness. They almost certainly will become far more intelligent than human beings—at least at certain tasks crucial for the functioning of human societies. In addition, these super-intelligent machines will be weaponized and made to operate on hair trigger warnings and largely autonomously without human supervision. They will also catalyze and re-energize human efforts to colonize and explore the solar system and ultimately interstellar systems.

Philosophically and theologically, the rise of intelligent machines raises fundamental questions about the personalist philosophical and metaphysical claims. Are we to accord the same dignity to machines as to humans or should I say human-hybrids, as we are all flesh-machine hybrids? If persons are ends in themselves and intelligent machines meet criteria for personhood what is the justification for using intelligent machines instrumentally? Either intelligent machines do not meet the criteria for personhood or human-hybrids are not persons. To begin to answer questions like these we need to get clear about the nature of machines in relation to persons.

Machines are less like persons and more like group entities. There is an interesting analogy to be drawn between machines and human groups. Machines (and groups) on the face of it are ontologically opposite to individual persons. Persons are ends in themselves. They are not to be treated as mere instrumental means to other ends. Machines (and groups) on the other hand are fashioned precisely in order to act as instrumental means to some end desired by persons. Thus, machines/groups negatively reflect the essence of persons as ends in themselves. In his "The question concerning technology"[16] Martin Heidegger argued that persons when they entertain and attempt to realize possible ideas typically act to facilitate the presencing or bringing-forth-to-actuality all kinds of free possibilities such as ideas, truths, artifacts, and even other persons. But the case of technology is different. When technological ideas are brought forth the thing or essence that moves from possibility into actuality is not something ready to act as instrument to a person's needs or desires, but instead appears as a "challenging – forth". When a new machine is made it does not simply and utterly conform to human needs. To operate the machine you need to adjust your body and mind to the machine's buttons, controls, properties, cycles, timing, and complexity. The machine requires the average person to adjust his lifeways to that of the artifact and puts the person in an existential stance Heidegger calls "standing reserve"—that is the person has to await and adjust to the user-friendly readiness of the artifact. The same can be said of human groups. When we first form a human group it is typically due to some instrumental need or purpose. We want the group to accomplish some goal we could not accomplish on our own whether it be to push a stalled car off the rod or to wage a war or build a city. We start with the idea that we will use the group to accomplish an end we desire. But all too often the group takes on a life of its own and we start adjusting our lives and purposes to that of the group's needs and purposes. We become involuntary adjuncts to the group.

Something similar often occurs with machines. A perfect example of this coercive power of machines is that we are all sitting at computer terminals tied to keyboards for hours at a time such that over very bodily physiologies, muscles and bones are shifting/adjusting to accommodate a sitting or sedentary existence demanded by the machine. In the modern age as tools and machines have become more and more complex, they begin to exert an ever more complete shaping influence on persons' possibilities. As technology's influence grows, the ability of persons to carry out their primary vocation of allowing truth-related possibilities to present or emerge into actuality is forgotten. This ability of technology (and groups) to put persons into an existential stance of standing reserve and forgetfulness toward revelatory truths Heidegger calls Gestell and Enframing. By enframing Heidegger seems to mean that technology shapes the ways people bring forth new truths and possibilities. Enframing imposes a uniformity, ordered mode of appearance, or bringing forth that induces a putting on-hold (standing reserve) of persons, of forgetfulness around the bringing forth of wild, free possibilities that is the true vocation of persons for Heidegger.

In his later publications Heidegger appears to indicate some agreement with the more apocalyptical views of technology associated with Ernst Junger.[17] For Junger technology cannot be characterized as essentially instrumental. It is not a neutral medium. It has a specific function: the total mobilization of all that is so that all that is can be transformed into overwhelming force and directed toward some goal. In times of war and more and more during the normal course of events for Junger that goal may be set by something or some Other, non-human quasi-intentional Titanic historical force or entity. It is not clear to this author what exactly Junger meant here. Perhaps this putative Titanic historical force is best understood as an egregore, a fictional monstrous Being discussed in literary circles. The egregore is created by crowds of people who invest it with superhuman powers. It is a personification of the collective group or hive minds of crowds of people all of whom want power to destroy an enemy. The emotional investment of these crowds builds up the supernatural being who then demands that humans sacrifice to them so that their powers increase. It is clear that Junger believes that people, when operating in crowds, relate to machines in the same way as they relate to these fictional egregores.

The paradigm case of crowd or mob-created egregoric machines apocalyptically interacting on the historical stage with catastrophic results for human beings is modern *war* where machines fight machines and human beings are just incidental players. The human beings on both sides believe they have the technical edge and that they are successfully using the machines to kill or dominate other human groups. But when viewed from a larger philosophic and historical perspective it quickly becomes clear that all warring parties have always believed these things down through the ages. They believe that they are utilizing machines, especially weapons, more humanely and effectively than their foes. But in any given conflict both human groups in the conflict are in fact to some significant extent obeying the mechanistic logic inherent in those weapons/machines as it is the people getting killed or enslaved on a massive but "orderly" machine-like scale. The winners are usually those groups who are more in service and enslaved to the machines in that they have larger technical capacities and better ability or industrial capacity to reproduce mechanized armies.

In human history at first it appeared as if the aim or goal of developing a technology was to subordinate "nature" to man. This seems like a reasonable goal: power over nature allows for better flourishing of human societies. Mere domination of nature, on the other hand, as we all now know, tends to create catastrophic ecological collapse, so it is unethical. But a reasonable amount of power over nature is defensible and sensible. But as man's technical capacities grew so too did man's desire to merge with the machine. As Karl Marx argued, the modern "worker" is emblematic in this regard. He becomes one with the machine, including the largest machine of them all—the totalitarian technocratic state. Once that merger between man and machine takes place then the true aim of the egregores, Titans or supra-human forces that rule technology becomes clear: the subordination of persons to the state machine and to the non-human forces that rule the machines. Junger's position seems to be unequivocally anti-technological. Yet he also argued that we can use the machines for our purposes as long as we remain existentially distant from them and refuse to be enslaved by them. In his 1980 novel *Eumeswil*[18] he presented the figure of the Anarch—an individual who guards his self-sovereignty like precious gold. The Anarch uses his intellectual wiliness to steer clear of the totalitarians and their mechanized forms of conformity and slavery. But the Anarch is no mere anarchist or Luddite. He is in favor of life—not mere ideas. He avoids the fanaticism of the reformers and the anti-reformers. He is *sui generis*—his own absolute individual. An end in himself—a person:

> The anarch is no individualist, either. He wishes to present himself neither as a Great Man nor as a Free Spirit. His own measure is enough for him; freedom is not his goal; it is his property. He does not come on as foe or reformer: one can get along nicely with him in shacks or in palaces. Life is too short and too beautiful to sacrifice for ideas, although contamination is not always avoidable. But hats off to the martyrs.
>
> (Junger, p. 209)

Junger's Anarch is eschatological personalism's Autarch. An autarch is a person capable of self-government. Indeed autarchy seems to be a fundamental prerequisite of personality in general given that freedom is integral to personality. You cannot assume responsibility for your actions unless you are capable of self-government. Self-government is another word for freedom of will. Since freedom of will is fundamental to eschatological personalism, to be an eschtatological personalist therefore is to be an autarch. Junger clearly is endorsing what we are calling autarchy as the only strategy we have that is capable of wisely handling the totalitarian state and its associated machines. Junger's analysis and attitude toward technology may help us to develop a new personalist philosophy, one that takes the challenge of technology seriously. A personalist needs first of all to understand that technology is never neutral: it seeks mobilization of force (in service to crowds, mobs, or masses of people) and ultimately that force will be injurious to persons. But that does not mean that we cannot use and benefit from machines. Even the most beneficent forms of technology tend to take on the power to shape our lives in all kinds of subtle ways. Take for example, a musical instrument. It can produce the most sublime happiness and well-being in its owner, but the more the owner uses it the more his life-world is altered to incorporate the instruments schedules, needs, and imperatives. At the level of a musical instrument the alteration in a person's lifeways seems harmless and even beneficent. But when we consider the countless machines we all encounter in our daily lives, and then the rise of the ubiquitous intelligent machines, the calculus of benefits and losses begins to change. When the ethos and imperatives of the machine are encoded and made operative in the modern technocratic state and we persons are required to subordinate ourselves to that ethos, then it is no longer unreasonable to ask whether we have become instruments for the machines. The Anarch/Autarch's task of avoiding assimilation into all modern forms of the machine, especially the technocratic state machine, becomes all the more difficult when the machine becomes super-intelligent and possibly conscious. That is a key task for a new personalism, to avoid subjugation and subordination to the machine and its technocratic state and ethos, via development of a new kind of person and a new relationship to technology and machines. I will argue only an eschatological personalism can do that.

Notes

1 see https://blogs.lse.ac.uk/usappblog/2017/09/23/thoughts-on-the-future-of-human-knowledge-and-machine-intelligence/
2 Burton, F.D. (2009). *Fire: The Spark that Ignited Human Evolution*. Albuquerque: University of New Mexico Press.
3 Schmidt, K. (2011). "Göbekli Tepe: A Neolithic Site in Southwestern Anatolia". In Steadman, Sharon R.; McMahon, Gregory (eds.). *The Oxford Handbook of Ancient Anatolia*. Oxford: Oxford University Press. pp. 917–936.
4 Boyce, Mary. (2001). *Zoroastrians*. 2nd ed. London: Routledge.
5 A thorough, sober assessment of the threats and potential benefits of super-intelligent machines can be found in books by Bostrom, N. *Superintelligence: Paths, Dangers, Strategies* (Oxford: Oxford University Press, 2014), and Tegmark, M. *Life 3.0: Being Human in the Age of Artificial Intelligence* (New York:

Alfred A. Knopf, 2017). Tegmark's Future of Life non-profit https://futureoflife. org/ is also a good source of information on AI ever-evolving capabilities.

6 A very good introduction to PPF history, theory, and applications can be found in Jakob Hohwy's *The Predictive Mind*. Oxford: Oxford University Press, 2013.

7 (https://deepdreamgenerator.com/).

8 (https://code.fb.com/ml-applications/deal-or-no-deal-training-ai-bots-to-negotiate/) 6.22.19.

9 See Kurzweil, R. *The Singularity Is Near: When Humans Transcend Biology* (New York: Penguin Group, 2005) for a key document in the rise of the transhumanist movement.

10 The following discussion of brain/cloud interface technologies is based largely on the review by Martins, N.R.B, Angelica, A., Chakravarthy, K., Svidinenko, Y., Boehm, F.J., Opris, I., Lebedev, M.A., Swan, M., Garan, S.A., Rosenfeld, J.V., Hogg, T., Freitas, R.A., Jr. (2019). Human Brain/Cloud Interface. *Frontiers in Neuroscience*,13: 112. Published online March 29, 2019. doi: 10.3389/fnins.2019.00112.

11 (https://futureoflife.org/data/documents/research_priorities.pdf).

12 See Zuboff, S. (2019). *The Age of Surveillance Capitalism: The Fight for a Human Future at the New Frontier of Power*. Cambridge: Public Affairs Publishing.

13 E.g., Waldfogel, J., Craigie, T.A., Brooks-Gunn, J. (2010). Fragile Families and Child Wellbeing. *Future Child. Fall* 20(2): 87–112.

14 See for example: Computer-Based Personality Judgments Are More Accurate than Those Made by Humans. Wu Y. et al. in *Proceedings of the National Academy of Sciences USA*, 112(4): 1036–1040; January 27, 2015. Psychological Targeting as an Effective Approach to Digital Mass Persuasion. Matz, S. C. et al. in *Proceedings of the National Academy of Sciences USA*, 114(48): 12714–12719; November 28, 2017. Deep Neural Networks Are More Accurate than Humans at Detecting Sexual Orientation from Facial Images. Kosinski M. and Wang, Y. in *Journal of Personality and Social Psychology*, 114(2): 246–257; February 2018.

15 See Tegmark (2015) for a good discussion of these possibilities.

16 Heidegger, M. (2013) *The Question of Technology and Other Essays*. New York: Harpers Perennial Modern Classics.

17 Blok, V. (2017). *Ernest Junger's Philosophy of Technology*. London: Routledge.

18 Junger, E. (1980, 1993). *Eumeswil*. New York: Marion Publishers.

2 Previous personalisms

The development of a new man and a new relationship with machines and technology requires that we develop a new form of personalism in order to protect the dignity and well-being of all persons in the coming age. In this chapter I review some key ideas of a number of classical or previous personalisms with a view to identifying those ideas we can use to build a new eschatological form of personalism—a personalism capable of meeting the challenge of the rise of intelligent machines. The aim is to develop a provisional conception of key concepts in personalism as well as key characteristics of personhood as these will need to be building blocks of an eschatological form of personalism. To pursue key ideas I will not proceed chronologically but instead follow the ideas themselves.

Explicit articulation of the modern personalist position began to take shape in the early 19th century and this story has been masterfully summarized in Jan-Olof Bengtsson's "Worldview of Personalism".[1] Bengtsson traces modern personalism's origins to the philosophical and theological ideas of F. H. Jacobi, the German idealists, and the British and Swedish personal idealists of the 19th century. In Bengtsson's account Jacobi reacted against the pantheism he detected in Spinoza and that surfaces in naturalism, materialism, and atheism. All forms of pantheism tend to submerge the individual into some larger totality that is given greater value than the individual. The ubiquity and power of the machine in the modern age tends also to assimilate the individual into larger groups and masses ordered by a kind of regimentary machine logic. Bengtsson also argues that many personalists emphasized that the abstractive function of understanding (as opposed to a more holistic faculty of reason) tended to create impersonal mechanistic modes of construal of the realities we find ourselves in. In addition to Jacobi and F.W.J. Schelling's key contributions to personalist thought in Germany, Andrew Seth Pringle-Pattison in Britain emphasized the fact that personality in itself contains built-in safeguards against dissolution into any absolute One or vice versa if God is personal his personal nature too would prevent his absorption into the many (pantheism). This theme of the source of personal dignity being linked to the autonomy of the individual will be central to personalism where autonomy is understood to be resistance to assimilation by the group, the whole, or God as well as resistance, on the other hand, to isolated possessive individualism. Healthy autonomy lies mid-way between these extremes. The personal is a liminal, in-between experience—a participation in what the Greeks called the metaxy.

Stitskin[2] provides a personalist reading of some strands of the Jewish philosophical tradition concerned with protection of individual autonomy and dignity. Stitskin notes that the revelation of God as personal—as a person—provided strong impetus for the idea that the personal was sacred. He argues that Judaism regards the self as oriented toward the transcendent as primary. It is a transcendent Being that reveals itself in self-consciousness. It is not a substance but a principle of unification realized in consciousness. This idea of unity in consciousness will be another central concern to eschatological personalism as it points directly to the source of that unity in "agency"—a source of autonomy and unity of consciousness. Stitskin discusses personalist themes in the Bible; in Talmud; and in the Rabbinic literature and reviews the work of several Jewish philosophers, including Abraham bar Hiyya, Saadia, Maimonides, Buber, Rosenzweig, and Hermann Cohen. Interestingly one theme that Stitskin discovers in all of these philosophers (of course with vastly differing emphases) is that in the very structure of the self, the personal is constituted via recognition of a call from beyond; of being as a gift and challenge that invites a response from beyond the self; from another personal reality. These personalist themes are also found in the work of Abraham Joshua Heschel and Emmanuel Levinas. The invitation to Being as gift and the call to personhood will be a fundamental characteristic of eschatological personalism.

A more recent form of a personalism built around agency, the metaphysics of freedom and possibility, and the "call" or vocation is David Norton's "Personal Destinies: A philosophy of ethical individualism".[3] Norton's eudaemonism is secular in nature and requires no transcendent God to issue the call. Instead, taking Socrates' Daemon as the paradigmatic example, the inner voice is conceived to be biologically innate, and when pursued reveals the individual's personal excellence that only he can exemplify. This individual excellence will fit into the universe of complementary excellences that make up the ideal community. Both Sartre and Nietzsche can be read in similar ways except that with Sartre the call is rooted literally in no-thing-ness or absolute freedom and the individual freely develops the project or purpose for which he is to live. These philosophers and many of the Jewish philosophers discussed by Stitskin also strongly emphasized political forces inimical to personal freedom and agency brewing in the 19th and early 20th centuries. For Nietzsche it was "herd" or mass group thinking and for Sartre it was totalitarian ideology as well as capitalist and class oppression.

It has often been said that modern forms of personalism emerged in reaction to the totalitarian ideologies of the 20th century, such as communism and fascism, but the philosophical spadework for personalism was largely done in the 19th century before the appearance of these totalitarian systems.[4] In addition to the philosophers mentioned above, I would argue that 19th- and early 20th-century forms of anarchism were an important source of insights into personality as well as political action in defense of individual autonomy. The anarchists not only produced original insights into the value of the individual but also unflinchingly opposed modern forms of submersion of the individual into the state. Many anarchists explicitly identified the dangers of fusing industrial machinery into the machinery of the political state. Lewis Mumford (1895–1990) who built upon the work of Peter Kropotkin (1842–1921) and other anarchist thinkers consistently referred to the danger of megamachines crushing the flesh and blood individual by constricting the biospace available to individuals and making the environment less and less "livable" for ordinary embodied flesh and blood humans. What Mumford called the "megamachine" reflected the alliance of state power with industrial age machines. Even now the megamachine operates to assimilate individuals into crowds and large masses of people to be used as cogs and components in the megamachine. It requires huge state bureaucracies and meticulous attention to accounting and standardization. The megamachine devalues persons and individuality while elevating people who have merged psychically with the machine such as bureaucrats and military leaders. These latter are then accorded cult status with masses and crowds of people exhibiting obsequious and servile behavior toward the "leader" who embodies the machine. The cogs in the machine, meanwhile, over time merge with the machine. Their sacred values begin to align with things like efficiencies, cost-effectiveness, precision, duplication, and standardization.

Almost all anarchists named the state as a key threat to genuine freedom and personality—something most personalists have failed to do. Anarchist thinkers (such as Max Stirner, who published his "Ego and its own"[5] in 1845), though they were marred by the failure to include love as constitutive of the individual's freedom, argued for an extreme form of individual autarchy, self-determination, and self-ownership which would protect against assimilation into the crowd.

Benjamin Tucker in America produced similar arguments for individual ownership of self or autarchy. William Godwin and John Stuart Mill in Britain produced very tightly argued political defenses of the individual liberty against the state. Bakunin in his God and the State[6] complained that to God was ascribed all goodness, truth, beauty, knowledge, and power while man was left bereft of anything of value. This ascription of all value to the transcendent is a danger for all eschatological visions. The End contains all value and the present is drained of all value. Transcendence overcomes immanence. This transcendence ideology becomes particularly dangerous when the transcendent reduces to the machine, particularly the state machine. Like other non-theists Bakunin's admirable rejection of the tendency to attribute all value to God, however, does not mean that we need to reject God altogether. For most personalists you don't throw the baby out with the bathwater. Instead you correct an impersonal notion of God…i.e. move him from an impersonal, impassable machine-like entity to a personal being. You restore and maintain the balance between a transcendent vision and a blessed Now.

In the 20th century personalism came of age with personalists appearing throughout the world despite (or perhaps in reaction to) the rise of totalitarian megamachine states throughout the world. Personalism in France came to prominence with the anarchist Proudhon's work and Charles Renouvier's "Personalism". Between World War I and II the French personalist movement revolved around a monthly journal, *Esprit*, founded by the Catholic author Emmanuel Mounier (1905–1950) and a group of friends in 1932. Echoing the "call" view of the person advocated by Jewish philosophers, biblical sources, and French existentialism, Mounier wrote "My person is the presence and unity of an eternal vocation in me, which calls me to surpass myself indefinitely".[7] The Russian exile Nikolai Berdyaev (1874–1948), working in Paris in the inter-war years alongside other philosophers (such as Gabriel Marcel and Jacques Maritain) sympathetic to personalist themes, developed a strikingly unique brand of personalistic thought in his many writings. He was also sympathetic with anarchism and very suspicious of the state. His perspective was Christian and tragic. He could sympathize with Nietzsche's reach for an aristocratic nobility but not endorse Nietzsche's atheism. At the center of Berdyaev's personalism was his emphasis on freedom. Even more than Sartre, Berdyaev conceived the person as free, and this constituted his autonomy, dignity, and nobility as well as his vulnerability to tragedy. Berdyaev was also aware of the development in history during the 20th century of a wholly new human relation to machines. In his lectures on "The meaning of history" given in Moscow in the early years of the Bolshevik revolution (around 1919; published in the West in 1936) Berdyaev wrote:

> I believe that the triumphant advent of the machine constitutes one of the greatest revolutions in human destiny. …It rips man away from the bowels of nature and changes the whole rhythm of his life. Formerly, an organic tie had existed between man and nature and his communal life had been governed by a natural rhythm. The machine radically modifies this relationship. It steps in between man and nature. It conquers not only the natural elements for the benefit of man, but also in the process man himself… It both liberates and enslaves him once again. …A new and mysterious force, alien to both man and nature now makes it appearance in human life; and this third, unnatural and nonhuman element acquires a terrible power over both man and nature.
>
> (Berdyaev, 1936; p. 135)[8]

Interestingly, Berdyaev believed that it was Christianity itself that prepared the way for the appearance of the machine in human life. The machine came into its own, in Berdyaev's telling of the history of the Christian West, during the Renaissance. Its way was prepared by the intense asceticism of the previous thousand years which was a direct project of the Christian church in Europe for over a thousand years. The monks created the machine in Berdyaev's story. While we can agree with Berdyaev that something new in the relation between man and machine emerges during the European Renaissance, we cannot accept his simple partition of history into an animistic period of immersion of the individual into nature; then a period of attempts to subjugate nature via asceticism during the Christian epoch; and finally the modern period, with the emergence of the machine into all areas of life of the individual. As argued above, humans have always used and depended on tools. The use of fire is an unimaginably ancient technology—perhaps two million years old. Fire is a technology that was used not just for processing food but also for creating all kinds of other artifacts. It allowed humans to colonize all areas of the globe including extremely cold areas. Humans began to dramatically alter the environment itself. They used fire to create their own ecological niches. They cleared whole forests and drove out all kinds of animal competitors and pests. Fire enabled humans to also colonize the night, thus altering biological rhythms and sleep phasing. Arguably this was when dreams and visions began to be valorized as crucial cultural artifacts or processes that acted as a source of strategic social and technical information within a tribe or community. Early human communities used information from dreams to develop rituals, ceremonies, clothing innovations, weapons, language elements, and much else besides. A new form of human being had to be developed to keep up with developments in fire technology. The fire-enabled processing of food (cooking) promoted dramatic changes in brain and body metabolism. New energetic sources for brain metabolism dramatically promoted growth of the brain beyond that expected of any other primate and this of course fundamentally altered what it meant to be a human person. Thus although Berdyaev's chronology was flawed, I believe, along with Berdyaev, that we are now entering a similarly revolutionary phase in our relation to technology—a phase that will also fundamentally alter what it means to be a human person. Berdyaev is correct it seems to me to emphasize the fact that in the modern age "A new and mysterious force, alien to both man and nature now makes it appearance in human life; and this third, unnatural and nonhuman element acquires a terrible power over both man and nature" (p. 136).

Out of all the personalists Berdyaev developed a distinctively eschatologically infused philosophy though he did not explicitly or clearly integrate the eschatological elements of his philosophy into his personalism. Berdyaev at one point called his philosophy an eschatological philosophy. He interpreted the Christian myth of the Fall as a fall into Time and "objectification". Objectification for Berdyaev was reducing the human personality or spirit to an object, a tool, or some means to other ends. To overcome objectification, we had to overcome time and see the human personality as anchored in freedom which is primordial and timeless. The world of objects comes to an end at the end of time, and then the Kingdom of God will reign, which is seen as the beginning of a new Aeon where subjectivity may be temporal but not objectified. The phenomenal world is temporary and illusory and the cause of suffering. The real world is the future Kingdom of God. The self is spirit, subjectivity, or non-objective. Creation is a human-divine collaborative act. God awaits man's creativity. When man responds creatively to God's invitation it is a breakthrough into eternity and thus is an eschatological act. Collaboration in creative acts with God is born of freedom and liberty. For Berdyaev however freedom is a primordial non-being or nothingness that is prior to God. He calls it the abyss. It is outside the space-time object world and breakthroughs into this world. Being is solidified or objectified freedom; its source is freedom or non-being. The human being or person represents a break in the natural object world as the person's essence is freedom and thus non-being. He is therefore a tragic figure. Man is both of this world and not of this world. He is therefore a microcosmos who contains both being and non-being in himself. The Christian revelation of the God-man speaks to the essence of human being. God gives birth to man so that man can give birth to God within. The imago Dei for Berdyaev is the personal or personality as it rises above natural life to point at the realm of eternity or timeless spirit. Personality and love are intimately related. To be in love with another means precisely to grasp the loved one's peculiar uniqueness, her identity and unity underlying all the perpetual changes she goes through. Love allows one to see the loved one's nobility of spirit even when that loved one is going through an utterly degrading process from the point of view of the world. This theme of love being the thing or process that fundamentally picks out the personal will be a constant for eschatological personalism. The eschatological personalism that I develop in this book will owe much to Berdyaev's philosophy but will eschew some of its gnostic themes such as freedom or the "abyss" being somehow prior to God.

Later French personalism largely neglected these eschatological themes and the philosophy of technology (though Jacques Ellul and Gabriel Marcel clearly articulated the dangers technology posed for human flourishing) leaving it to post-modernist figures such as Foucault and Ricoeur to chart the machine and state-enabled regimentation of human bodies and psyches. Berdyaev's emphasis on agency and freedom as central to personality also needed to be fleshed out, developed, and related to other key markers of the personal such as meaning- and value-seeking. The philosopher Paul Ricoeur (1913–2005)[9] was arguably personalist in his outlook. He argued that self-understanding was never an unmediated process but had to occur by means of language or at least signs or symbols of some kind. Self-understanding was therefore self-interpretation and what was needed was a new hermeneutically inspired anthropology. Man is the interpreter because language is central to his being. For Ricoeur the unity of the personal comes from self-interpretation supported by a tradition or community. The form self-interpretation takes in Ricoeur is narrative understanding or under-standing via narrative schemes. The unity of the personal therefore consists in narrative. Narrative is a kind of experimentation with possible worlds. Each narrative presents us with what might have been—what might have happened when and who did what to whom. We derive meanings via pro-duction of these narratives. They are like elaborate counterfactual imagin-ings where we experiment with alternative scenarios in order to evaluate what caused what and what to do next. We understand the significance of things via these narratives. They are deeply embedded in human nature and dream-like simulations of possible realties. Narrative demonstrates that we are visioning, dreaming animals.

The personal is special in that it alone in the universe produces "mean-ings" and can only be understood via narrative enquiry or interpretation. The meaning-producing self inhabits the intentional order while another modality of the self inhabits the non-intentional physical order. These two modalities of self, though opposite in many ways, have to be construed as complementary as well, as intentionality is meaningless without objects and others in the world to refer to, and conversely without intentionality the physical order would not really be the physical order. It would not be anything for any mind. Both modalities of self are required to make the personal possible. Ricoeur calls these modalities the idem self and ipse self. The self's idem-identity is what makes the self an individual object among other physical objects while its ipse-identity is what accounts for its ability to create meaning. Thus, the ipse-identity carries agentic aspects of the per-sonal. We will see this theme of the polarity within the personal, the oscil-lation between an idem, inward looking pole grounded in immanence and an ipse meaning-making, outward looking pole anchored in transcendence, play out in many personalist writings, and it will play a role in eschatolog-ical personalism as well.

With regard to person as both a meaning-seeking and value-seeking indi-vidual R. H. Lotze's (1817–1881) in Germany made seminal contributions to axiological approaches to personalism. In Edmund Husserl's phenom-enological methods, Max Scheler (1874–1928), Dietrich von Hildebrand (1889–1977), and Edith Stein (1891–1942) in Germany built on Husserl's methods to investigate the nature of ultimate value and personhood as well as subjectivity. All three emphasized the central role of love in elevating the individual's perceptual abilities in order to see and grasp things of real value including one's own personhood.

Another source of European personalistic thought concerning the themes of value, meaning, agency, and vocation grew up around the Catholic Uni-versity of Lublin. The future Pope John Paul II, Karol Wojtyła, then studying in Lublin became interested in Max Scheler's axiological ethics and the phe-nomenology of the personal and ended up doing his doctoral dissertation on Scheler's ethics of values, which he presented in 1953. Wojtyła, who was also influenced by the writings of another of Husserl's disciples, von Hildebrand, produced two significant personalist books, *Love and Responsibility* (1960) and *The Acting Person* (1962), as well as numerous essays, lectures, and articles on ethics and personhood. In *The Acting Person* Wojtyła shows that the will, and therefore freedom of the will, cannot be thought coherently simply in terms of a psychic power. Instead control of the will implies and requires the person—an acting person, who selects and chooses freely only when he does so according to principles of love. Given that personhood inheres, for Wojtyła (as it did for Scheler), in the person's actions there is no infinite regress onto smaller and smaller homunculi in this philosophy. A person can act coherently and therefore with some unity only if he acknowledges and is capable of appreciating a hierarchy of values with love or God as the topmost value and other persons in a community of love as primary.

As with many of other personalist thinkers/philosophers Wojtyła produced some very interesting reflections on solitude/privacy as crucial for realizing personality, value, and right relationships with others. In his lectures on the theology of the body as marked by the personal or the nuptial, Wojtyła reflects on the Genesis creation story wherein Adam is created in the image and likeness of God. Adam is marked off from all other creation and creatures in that he names them and understands their essential natures yet at the same time he feels incomplete and that it is not good to be alone. He is aware of his aloneness, his solitude, and that this solitude is the root of his self-awareness and his knowledge of creation. It also is the root of his capacity for relatedness as he becomes aware that it is not good to be alone—that there is a yearning for something more. Adam therefore manifests this double nature as a consequence of his solitude: he simultaneously experiences a dawning self-awareness and knowledge of all of creation as well as awareness of infinite yearning for something more of ultimate value. Adam's primeval state contained that dual nature of the personal with one pole anchored on his solitude (immanence) and the other focused outwardly yearning for an Other. There is no authentic personal that does not include both poles or movements: one toward immanence and the other toward transcendence. The two poles are synthesized in the act of Love. Adam's solitude reflects God's essence as God too has knowledge of All and by the very fact that He is Love, he too exists in act as he totally gives himself in love to others as gift.

Wojtyła's later election as Pope contributed strongly to the spread of personalist thought, especially among Catholic thinkers. Czesław Stanisław Bartnik, Bogumil Gacka, and others in Poland, John Crosby in the United States, and John Cowburn in Australia have developed personalist philosophies consistent with the eschatological orientation being developed here.

John Crosby in particular has mounted a very complete defense and presentation of personalist philosophy especially in the tradition of the axiological philosophers like Scheler, von Hildebrand, and Pope John Paul II. Crosby's starting principles are as follows: persons are ends in themselves and never mere means to some other purpose or end—no matter how elevated that end is construed to be. Persons are wholes of their own and never mere parts. Thus, a person is not a mere piece of the state or of God or of the community or of any other group.

Many religious people in the West see the individual as a mere emanation, or dim reflection of, or a piece of God. Or they seek assimilation or dissolution into divinity—they want to become God or dissolve their selves into God. Theosis is held up as an ideal to be sought after. The old saying in Christianity that "God became Man so that man can become God" speaks to this yearning to overcome the apparent finitude of the human personality. Some versions of Buddhism and Hinduism likewise seek dissolution of individual consciousness branding "separateness" as an illusion—a pernicious illusion because it is construed as the origin of desire. But according to eschatological forms of personalism desire is a good thing and dissolution of separateness is not a worthy goal for a human being. Love is only possible because separateness and distinction between persons are real. At the base of personality is an oscillation between separateness/immanence and belonging/transcendence. You cannot have real individuals without that oscillatory activity. There has to be a resistance to belonging as well as a yearning to belonging. The resistance to instantiation[10] into any larger whole constitutes the person's metaphysical ultimacy. Persons are incommunicably their own, separate worlds and never mere specimens. Finally, each person belongs to himself and not to any other.[11] Clearly, if the person is unique, incommunicably his own and an end in himself then his value is infinite and thus personality is an ultimate value.

Personalism has also been represented, to varying degrees, in many other countries including South American, Asian, and Middle Eastern countries. The Argentinian philosopher Francisco Romero's (1891–1962) Theory of Man[12] contained strong personalist themes. Jose Ortega y Gasset emphasized the historicity of the human person. Juan Manuel Burgos is a Spanish philosopher and the President of the Spanish Association of Personalism, an institute dedicated to development and promotion of personalism. He has published personalist interpretations of the philosophies of Maritain and Wojtyła. He has also emphasized that key to personhood is a center of affectivity typically referred to as the heart where apperception of value fundamentally takes place. It is this mystery of love (rooted in the center of the person or heart) that both perceives infinite value and picks out the uniquely personal that needs attention in any adequate personalist philosophy. We will see that an eschatological personalism also has love as its central metaphysical principle. Love synthesizes the two poles (immanence/transcendence) in the personality's dual nature. It creates the heart or still point at the center of the personality.

The Scottish philosopher John Macmurray (1891–1976) developed a unique form of personalism that (like Cicero and Montaigne before him) emphasized the love involved in friendship. Friendship is not mere altruistic love toward another. Instead it is a radical giving away of one's self to another. Friendship would not be possible without this capacity of individuals to give all of themselves in love to another and that radical gift is not possible unless the personal is real. To be a friend is to be yourself for another. We think we understand the personal but it is not yet really understood, just as friendship too is not understood. The personal is characterized by infinities in the sense that the urge toward the other (transcendence) is unquenchable and the urge towards interiority (immanence) is equally never-ending. We have attempted to model the personal in terms of mechanical metaphors (the self as machine) and organic metaphors (the self as process or development) but these metaphors cannot account for friendship and the boundless capacity of the self to utterly pour itself out—even to die for another.

The giving away of the self to another in friendship paradoxically does not diminish the self but enriches it. If you can completely pour yourself out and yet not be diminished, there must be something infinite in you, in the personal. The value that friends see in one another and that they each sacrifice themselves for is precisely the friendship which is a union that preserves the utterly unique individuality of each of the friends. We become truly unique and individual when we give ourselves away in love for another. Personality as love or eros is the fundamental capacity for self-transcendence. It is always surpassing itself, and in this capacity lies its this-worldly effects. Macmurray also emphasized that giving one's self away constitutes the self as agent; it is the form agency takes as personal.

We turn now to American forms of personalism. While European personalism was largely Catholic in inspiration American personalism was largely Protestant in inspiration.

The Boston University personalist tradition

The founder of the Boston personalist tradition was Borden Parker Bowne (1847–1910). Bowne was a Methodist minister who had studied under the personalist philosopher Rudolf Hermann Lotze in Germany. Bowne's late book *Personalism*,[13] published in 1908, is a lucid summary of his philosophy and a catalog of the failures of impersonalism in philosophy. Bowne is rightly considered the founder of Boston University (BU) personalism because he emphasized the irreducible unity and wholeness of the personality. The unity of the person comes from an agency that is sovereign over memory and over the entire temporal order of the person:

> Each new experience leaves the soul other than it was; but, as it advances from stage to stage it is able to gather up its past and carry it with it, so that at any point, it possesses all that it had been. It is this fact only which constitutes the permanence and identity of the self.[14]

The agentic-like unitary consciousness is also mind as it imposes order on the flux of experiences that it either discards or transfers into meanings for the person agent. The fact that mind imposes some order on sensory experiences suggests that the world is intelligible for the agent intellect. This is confirmed by the successes of the sciences. Intelligibility of the universe, in turn, suggests that mind/mentality is core to reality and the universe. Intelligibility supports the view that mentality or something like it must be unified, must be able to stand in some judgment of the universe, and must be part of the basic stuff of the universe. Bowne also argues, like his colleague across the river in Cambridge Josiah Royce, that the possibility of error also implies that the mind has an innate ability to discern intelligibles and the truth about things. The mind must discover truth by modeling it and then comparing the model against the facts as they currently stand. The error between model and the facts yields cumulatively better approximations to truth. The ability to err and to cognize truth also implies that persons are free. Endorsing a kind of agent-causation, autarchic view of causality Bowne argued that "By freedom in our human life we mean the power of self-direction, the power to form plans, purpose, ideals and to work for their realization".[15] Freedom is essentially the ability to choose among genuine alternatives or possibilities. In the realm of knowledge-seeking that ability to choose which possibilities to realize, to discern the truth, confirms man's freedom. If there were no advance in the sciences there would be no substantial proof for man's freedom. The ability to not just choose the truth but to prefer the truth underlies value apprehension and ultimately ethics.

Bowne interacted with the great triumvirate of American philosophers at that time, all of whom were arguably personalist in their orientations.[16] These were William James (1842–1910), Josiah Royce (1855–1916), and Charles Sanders Peirce (1839–1914). Bowne (and the great triumvirate) drew as well on the work of the idealist personalist George Holmes Howison (1836–1916) to improve his ideas. Bowne gathered a group of talented disciples who carried on his work in a second generation. Among these second-generation personalists was Edgar Sheffield Brightman (1884–1953) whose work on the "shining present" and "illuminating absent" will be examined for its implications for an eschatological personalism in more detail below. Other second-generation Boston personalists included Albert C. Knudson (1873–1953), Francis J. McConnell (1871–1953), and Ralph T. Flewelling (1871–1960). Ralph Tyler Flewelling co-founded *The Personalist*,[17] the journal that would serve as the forum for American personalism until the 1980s. In 1915, he published *Personalism and the Problems of Philosophy: An Appreciation of the Work of Borden Parker Bowne*.[18] In 1927 Knudson published *The Philosophy of Personalism*.[19] Third-generation Boston personalists included Peter Bertocci (1910–1989) who developed some of Brightman's ideas (and edited Brightman's final book "Person and Reality") but added many of his own, particularly bringing in scientific psychology on the person. More than any other Boston personalist Peter Bertocci engaged the developing science of psychology to gain insights into personhood. His 1963 book with Richard Millard "Personality and the Good"[20] went deeply into the psychological literature to describe developmental antecedents of the person as well as social psychological perspectives on apprehension of value—specifically "dependable values"—values that are judged to be best after systematic criticism of their relation to other relevant values. Bertocci and Millard also provided a complex explication of Brightman's ethical system—a topic I discuss in a later chapter on eschatologically informed ethics.

In his *Religion as Creative Insecurity*[21] Bertocci argued against standard Freudian interpretations of religion as a mere security blanket for fearful children. Instead religion promotes an enduring, mature form of generativity and creativity which is antithetical to tranquilized forms of emotional "security". Positive, mature forms of creativity also involve love of self and others. Insecurity and suffering can be redemptive to the extent that it issues in creativity that enriches self and others. In his 1967 *Sex, Love and the Person*,[22] Bertocci argued for the centrality of the personal to sexual fulfillment. At the height of the so-called "sexual revolution" of the 1960s Bertocci argued against a merely "biomorphic" conception of sex and noted that it needed to be personalized to be enriching. This approach to sexuality is remarkably similar to "theology of the body" developed by the personalist Pope John Paul II in the 1980s.

In his 1970 collection of essays *The Person God Is*,[23] Bertocci took personalism into the exploration of creativity as a central component process of the personal. Like Berdyaev before him, Bertocci argued that persons are co-creators with God. Subjectivity is a unity of experiences like wanting, thinking, planning, oughting, etc. in a single span of time encompassing the present, past, and future. The ability to transcend time and range over the entire past, present, and potential future life-episodes of an individual life in order to derive meaning is a mark of the agentic personal. Like Bergson, Bertocci calls this the personal form of temporality duration. Experiences occur to an agent in a temporal mode. These experiences of subjectivity are not created bit by bit but are given whole in an interpenetrating NOW. They are dynamic, cumulative, and novel mental items with the growth of experiences over time. While content cumulates and changes, cognitive structures do not change—thinking does not turn into sensing and sensing does not turn into emotions and so on. The activity-structure of mentality/subjectivity remains the same indirectly indicating a permanent agent behind the flux. He calls this the *unitas multiplex*. The *unitas multiplex* therefore exhibits flux and novelty in its contents but relative sameness in its structure. Its temporalist, dynamic structure, however, implies that the self/agent is always gathering up its past and projecting its projects into the future, thus reminding us of Bowne's apparent agent process that transcended and derived meaning from the temporally defined experiences of the individual. These projections are compared against current states of affairs in order to motivate growth.

As we will see with Brightman's account of subjectivity, Bertocci also suggests that the continuity of sameness despite change due to memory may also be related to a control or agentic process in subjectivity that selects some contents over others in order to project a desired future. The desired future is compared against the current state of affairs. Unity and internal conflict emerge from this is-ought comparison process. The agentic self can appropriate via its agentic control of attentional processes and its ability to project desired states of affairs and to compare these against current states, elements of the stream of consciousness such that some are appropriated as past and some as future anticipations and so forth. Thus, a major source of continuity within subjectivity is the telic tendency in mental life—that is prospection or future-oriented purposive striving wherein the future is creatively envisioned and compared to current content in order to better realize future "oughts". Agentic selective processes and telic strivings constitute a unity of intrinsic activities that are constantly testing their creative response potential against a constantly changing environment. The self or the person is not a present added to a past or a present moving into a future. Instead the person is an active unity able to use agentic control processes to use the past to creatively synthesize experiences in the "now" and to envision desired futures, to compare current affairs against these desired futures so as to maintain its unity and grow.

Like Bowne, Brightman, and Royce before him Bertocci argues[24] that the fact that cognitive error occurs suggests that the personal involves a search and awareness of truth. The fact that there can be state of affairs that is nonetheless in error is also quite mysterious. It suggests that the essence of mentality and the personal lies in the ability to refer beyond the current state of affairs to either a truthful state of affairs or a "possible world" or a non-existent state of affairs. Right at the heart of mentality, of intentionality, therefore, is this ability or this defect to conjure or project possible worlds, including a false world of nothingness or error as well as the ability to find truth. This cognitive ability to project or construct fictive worlds lies at the heart of mentality, agency, and the unity of consciousness. These claims will be central to eschatological personalism.

L. Harold DeWolf (1905–1986), Georgia Harkness (1891–1974), and Walter Muelder (1907–2004) among others further developed the social ethics of personalism. The psychologist and philosopher Mary Whiton Calkins (1863–1930) can be considered a second-generation Boston personalist as well. She worked in Boston at the time, interacted with Bowne and others (though not at BU), and called herself an absolutistic personalist. She argued that dreams were an important component of personality and produced important work on the psychology of dreams as well as philosophy of personalism.

Martin Luther King Jr studied under the third-generation personalists (as well as Brightman right before he died) at BU and credited the experience with shaping his worldview.

> I studied philosophy and theology at Boston University under Edgar S. Brightman and L. Harold DeWolf…It was mainly under these teachers that I studied Personalistic philosophy—the theory that the clue to the meaning of ultimate reality is found in personality. This personal idealism remains today my basic philosophical position. Personalism's insistence that only personality—finite and infinite—is ultimately real strengthened me in two convictions: it gave me metaphysical and philosophical grounding for the idea of a personal God, and it gave me a metaphysical basis for the dignity and worth of all human personality.[25]

Fourth-generation Boston-linked American personalists include Carol Sue Robb, (1945-), Harold Oliver (1930–2011), John H. Lavely, Erazim Kohak (1933-), and Rufus Burrow (1951-) whose history of personalism gave us this generational genealogy.[26] Carol Sue Robb carried personalist insights into her work in feminist thought in California. Harold Oliver criticized trends in personalist thought that seemed to assume a substance-based ego as core to personhood. Oliver developed a relational metaphysics of the person. John Lavely ably defended the idea of a personal God and Rufus Burrow went on to write a landmark *Critical Introduction to Personalism* emphasizing its role in development of social ethics. Burrow has also written profound works on personalist themes in the thought of Martin Luther King Jr.

Kohak is a Czech philosopher who after spending years at BU returned to his home country the Czech Republic after the fall of the Eastern Bloc countries beginning with the fall of the Berlin Wall in 1989. Like the Russian personalist Nikolai Berdyaev, Kohak insists that we need to add suffering/tragedy to the list of essential traits of the person if we are to really grasp the meaning of the personal. Kohak's masterpiece *The Embers and the Stars*[27] integrates, in my view, the personalist vision with "Nature" and the impersonal cosmos. The logos within, which partially defines the personal, is the same as the logos without which informs the cosmos itself so there can be no personal realm without nature.

The personal is the gift of nature. To the extent that machines destroy Nature they destroy personality. The bond between the personal and nature can be nourished with solitude and wilderness. Solitude within wilderness is not exactly alone-ness. There is a You out there, addressing you personally, accepting and justifying your subjectivity. That mind or Logos that is nature supports and makes possible your subjectivity. Solitude therefore is gift.

> For most of us even to think of solitude as gift requires an effort…. we are convinced that truth is in communication…Philosophy must

speak...but...it must first hear and see and that is not a task for crowds and committees. The consensus of a crowd can constitute a conventional world far too readily, far too soon...The intersubjective consensus establishes something very like a collective solipisim...A philosophy which begins with a consensus will not easily penetrate beyond the shell of our collective monad...To do that we must first suspend that consensus in the radical brackets of solitude.

(Kohak, 1987; pp. 34–35)

That solitude should occur in wilderness:

Here nature presses in. It is too vast for the human to outshout it, too close for him to withdraw from it into speculation. The world the human confronts here is not the phenomenal world, a convention of human community or a speculative construct...It is the...thing in itself, present to be acknowledged, making its own demands. Solitude is the great liberating gift from which philosophy can be born, not as a way of seeming but as the way of truth.

(Kohak, 1987; p. 35)

"The affirmation of the ontological primacy of meaningful being for which I would revive the designation 'personalism'...calls for nothing less than an act of confidence in the ultimate reality of persons and the ultimate veridicality of individual consciousness" (Kohak, 1987; p. 133). Despite its capacities for self-deception, error, and evil, human consciousness is capable of grasping the real, the true, and the beautiful. We attain to ultimate values via human consciousness or the personal. Without the personal or persons, life would be meaningless.

The category proper to persons is a moral category whose vocabulary is respectfulness. People in ages past are no longer embodied humans but they retain a presence in our lives that commands respect and is therefore personal. When humans treated the cosmos and nature as a You or personal, we also felt the need to honor the memory of landscapes, objects, or even totem animals. Even today we create all kinds of rituals that are designed to honor the memories of persons who came before us, presumably because they remain bearers of value and meaning both for us and for others who will come after us. Kohak would have us extend the category of the personal to nature. We experience nature as accepting of us, and at least for a time as supporting us as bearers of value. Nature is alive, and it nurtures us. Its very intelligibility tells us that it is not foreign to us; rather that it embodies something that is also in us: namely mentality, mind, or logos. It should not be construed in merely instrumental terms. Kohak criticizes the Boston personalists for treating nature all too often in purely instrumental terms. But according to Kohak the personalist worldview implies a non-instrumental stance toward nature because it too is personal. We need to recover the sense that the personal is an ultimate category that inheres in ourselves and in nature.[28]

Meanwhile Walter George Muelder (1907–2004) helped to develop the field of social ethics and, via his appointments at both BU and the University of Southern California, helped bridge the gap between the Bostonian and Californian schools. In 1983 he published a book of essays written over his entire career[29] in which he deploys his view of persons as irreducible historical wholes of meaning and value and the implications of that view for social ethics.

I turn now to an in-depth consideration of some of the key ideas of Edgar Sheffield Brightman whom I consider to be important for development of an eschatological personalism. What Brightman gives us is a rich account of agency and subjectivity.

Brightman

Brightman built upon Bowne's defense of the intelligibility of the universe arguing that the categories (space, time, and number) "...would fall apart into unrelated fragments of vanishing experience" if there were no personality to unify them into a rational or truth-seeking whole.[30] To get at the essence of the personal "Remove from personality those aspects that are peculiar to man and consider it in its essential nature..."[31]

> Remove desire for victory in war, but leave desire for the highest and best; remove the particular local environment of this or that man's experience, but leave the power to interact with any environment; remove the memories of this man's particular weaknesses and sins, but leave memory as the unifying power binding past and present; remove petty and selfish purposes, but leave purpose as the movement of reality into the future; remove the traits of my partly integrated personality but leave the experience of the unity of consciousness as indivisible wholeness-and one then has in personality a clue to universal being, a genuine first principle.[32]

In this passage we get very clearly expressed the eschatological personalist position concerning the issue of unity of consciousness and argued for in this book. Unity of consciousness indicates the essence of the personal as act or agency. Unlike everything else in this world it is a whole and indivisible. It cannot be broken down into parts (although it has internal structure). It is wholly agentic in the sense of leaving behind potentiality. Since it is whole nothing more in it needs to be actualized. It is actual, pure actuality and therefore not of this world, but belongs to eternity. The personal is anchored in eternity. Valuation of the highest and best, power to interact with the environment, memory as unifying and cumulative knowledge, purpose or end-directedness, unity of consciousness, and indivisible wholeness...

If you add to these fathomless interiority and incommensurability these are the traits that characterize subjectivity—one of the basic realities of the universe. Subjectivity is not mere passivity. Instead it issues from its essence as pure actuality or agency. Receptivity is also not inimical to agency. Instead it depends on agency as agency is a prerequisite for receptivity—without an agent to receive a gift no gift giving is possible. In summary, for Brightman the personal was rational (or at least potentially rational), purposive, social, free, unified, whole, agentic, and rooted in experience.[33]

In his last book *Person and Reality*[34] Brightman lays out his theory of personality and the relation of subjectivity to the categories and other "realms of being". The book was unpublished at his death in 1953. In a great service to philosophy Peter Bertocci, Jannette Newhall, and Brightman's younger son, Robert E. Brightman, compiled his final papers, edited them, and ensured the work's publication.[35] In *Person and Reality*, Brightman argues that the philosopher has to begin with the empirical facts of experience which are given to him/her in the immediate present. "The situation experienced or the shining present contains all presently observable consciousness-all sensations, images, reasoning, loves, hates, fears, and hopes of Now, all conations, strivings and efforts, desires, aversions".[36] Brightman notes that the shining present involves a perpetual perishing or falling away of experiences and therefore involves experience and data that are absent. He calls these absent experiences the illuminating absent as they all inform his experiences of the shining present. The memory of the past influences the perishing present as does desire and striving toward the future. Brightman here tends toward the Bergsonian view of consciousness as duration or essentially temporal experience. "...however fragmentary it is, it contains a real duration-a present-past-future time span grasped in one whole experience".[37]

The shining present and the illuminating absent inter-relate—one requires the other. They are the "given" but the shining present and illuminating absent also contain elements that are produced by thought and not merely given. How do they inter-relate? Any given shining present is a first-person experience of a complex unity of consciousness that is not directly accessible to other minds and that has a unique relation to past and future experiences (presumably a relation of appropriation or "ownership" though Brightman is not clear here). A shining present is indexical, focused inwardly and toward the given or the immanent. The illuminating absent, on the other hand, is referenced to the beyond and the transcendent (e.g. in form of memories and anticipations). The given-ness of the shining present is innocent insofar as nothing can be inferred from the mere given-ness of experience. Nevertheless, thought is also given, and when it is active, reason can guide thought and inferences can then be brought to bear upon the given. The first-person perspective so characteristic of the shining present captures the centrality of affect, qualia, the feeling of "what it is like" to be in that shining present. First-person experience is also private experience.

We cannot directly experience the qualia of a different shining present. We communicate with other minds without a diminution of the content of either mind so shining presents are not windowless monads.

The complex unity of the shining present implies that the I that is the shining present experiences its content all at once as a unified whole—a fact that Brightman calls self-identity. Epistemically the shining present is a source of the absent. Man's knowledge is rooted in first-person experience. The illuminating absent is a source of knowledge concerning the appearance of the shining present. The shining present contains within itself elements that allow it to check the veridicality of its own experiences in the form of evidence of an illuminating absent wherein is integrated into the shining present elements absent from the present, including memories and purpose. This evidential element in experience allows the shining present to carry on experiments to further check veridicality of experiences. Because there are other shining presents in the world every shining present also has an outgoing extrinsically oriented impulse that becomes the illuminating absent and imbues the shining present with an interpersonal capacity.

The present set of experiences is largely the result of past memories and anticipatory desires—largely but not completely. Therefore, we have to conclude that while the absent is causally related to the present it does not exhaust or totally account for the present. In addition, agency or freedom can control elements of the present via selection of some elements over others and so on. Key to the shining present is the awareness of possibilities or anticipations. These future-oriented cognitions characterize the purpose oriented and end-directedness of subjectivity. The past sometimes influences these possibilities but often there are possibilities that are not related to the past and therein lies a core element of freedom within subjectivity.

The shining present contains experiences wherein control or directedness of attention is felt...we do not just passively experience the flow of elements in the shining present. Instead we can within the shining present emphasize some over other experiences and so forth. It is far from clear what does the controlling, however. Some aspects of the shining present can control other aspects of the shining present and these other aspects that are not under voluntary control are simply given to consciousness. "Every moment of actual experience is an indivisible whole of some degree of activity controlling some aspects of the Given...every shining present is a whole of experience which may be described as a control of the Given".[38] It therefore follows that within the shining present there is an agentic ability to accept or not accept the Given—to control, shape, synthesize, or inhibit the Given. In addition, controlling the given allows for construction of predictions or models of desired future states and to compare these models or predictions against current sensory facts presented in the shining present. The modeling and comparison process support the sense that consciousness is unified as the model and the comparison process are both produced by the single agent from within the shining present. The models produced by the agent are compared against the "Given", and these operations on the Given constitute a major portion of the activity of the shining present.

The Given is composed of the rational and the nonrational given. The rational given are things like Plato's or Whitehead's eternal objects, objective values, principles of logic and moral norms, and so forth. The nonrational given are things like contingent or accidental or chance sense qualities, desires, emotions, pains, or sheer brute fact. Brightman seems to have something like Peirce's Firstness in mind here. The shining present exhibits several levels of unity from the simple unanalyzed level of immediacy to analyzed immediacy to causal uniformity to normative control, functional unity, and then finally the level of whole experience.

The task of the shining present is one of agency—to explore the realm of the Given (both rational and nonrational) and to control the realm of nonrational Given. Out of these operations on the given emerges the sense of identity. "It is the categorical property of the shining present to be and to require personal identity".[39] Personal identity must be considered one of the primordial categories of some specific realms of being (e.g. the realm of Persons of course). Other categories, such as time, change/identity, actuality-potentiality, apply to all realms of being (essence, nature, persons, values).

Time is not mere duration as space, obligations, and objects endure but are not time. Time is an order with a past-present-future structure.[40] Relative to any present the past is determinate and the future is potential. All kinds of human cognitions depend on time. Purpose depends on time as does memory. In memory the shining present of today's experience is transcended in that memory unites into a whole set of experiences that are not now. The illuminating absent includes another moment of transcendence via communication with other shining presents. Temporally speaking the illuminating absent is unbegun and unending duration in which may be discovered truths (via communication with others and via self reasoning, etc.) that are true for all times. Thus the illuminating absent is a road toward science and ultimate religious truths. Also within the temporality of the shining present are the anticipations and possibilities of future-oriented cognition. These too include an element of transcendence as the I is taken out of the now and placed into a liminal "future" where possibles reign.

Pulling all this together Brightman sums up his treatment of the personal as follows:

> A personality is a complex but self-identifying, active, selective, feeling, sensing, developing experience, which remembers its past (in part), plans for its future, interacts with its subconscious processes, its bodily organism and its natural and social environment, and is able to judge and guide itself and its objects by rational and ideal standards.[41]

The Boston personalists were particularly insightful when it came to the problem of explaining the unity of the consciousness. Bowne, Bertocci, and Brightman all linked the primacy of personality to the phenomenon of unity in consciousness, which was described as a free, agentic process. That agency gave the mind the capacity to compare what is to what ought to be. Unity was related to ethics. The creation of a model of the desired state of affairs as experienced as a whole bout or episode of consciousness and the unconscious comparison between what is and what is desired or ought to be not only motivated growth and change but also contributed to that same sense of unity of personality. The agentic future ideal self was held to be outside of time and therefore able to reach back to the now and the illuminating absent to unify the entire consciousness into one whole.

Personalism within early scientific psychology

William Stern (1871–1938) was perhaps the first psychologist who took the issue of scientific investigation of the person seriously. Lamiell's intellectual biography of Stern[42] captures Stern's insight into the problem of the individual in the following quote: "Every individual is a singularity, a one-time existing being, nowhere else and never before present...this distinct last kernel of being... which reveals the individual to be thus and so,...is unclassifiable and incommensurable...".[43]

Stern clearly understood essential aspects of the person but he nevertheless studied the person all his life. Just because something is unique does not mean it cannot be studied. Just because something is incommensurable does not mean it cannot be cognized even though it does mean it cannot be classified. We can cognize the unique via analogy with other things we are familiar with.

Wilhelm Windelband introduced the contrast between knowledge construction that emphasizes the general (nomothetic) and that which focuses on the particular (idiographic).[44] Though much has been made of this idiographic versus nomothetic divide in psychology, when examined closely it really is a specious concept. In a fundamental sense, everything that we study, whether it be persons, objects, events, processes, or whatever, is really unique, distinctive, and irreplaceable. Even the lowly factory made widget is unique given that it was punched out of the machine at a slightly different time and therefore in a slightly different manner than all other widgets. The fact that things come into and pass out of existence at different times makes everything unique and irreplaceable so we are always examining unique objects in order to derive general, lawlike knowledge from them. The basis of all human knowledge is therefore in a basic sense idiographic. But clearly the term idiographic is pointing to our everyday usage of the concept unique. Widgets are not unique (because they really are replaceable) while persons are unique and irreplaceable.

We can therefore take advantage of this fact and focus attention on the unique instance, or we can aggregate such experiences on any basis we wish. We can aggregate based on shared attributes or shared time stamps.

Aggregation is the method favored by scientific psychology up to now. While aggregation is entirely legitimate and absolutely indispensable, it is not the only strategy we can pursue. Indeed if we are interested in those aspects of the person that resist aggregation then obviously we need to supplement aggregative techniques with other techniques.

When we take the non-aggregative, idiographic approach to persons the main thing we should study according to Stern was what he called the *unitas multiplex*—the unity of identity/consciousness displayed by the individual despite a multitude of differing experiences the person undergoes. The person maintains a unity across time and across diverse sense impressions. How is that unity accomplished? For Stern the unity does not arise out of phenomenal experiences. These experiences are experienced as unified in consciousness but what creates that unity? It is not simple association of experiences; it is not association in time and unity was not imposed from outside consciousness. If the "I" creates the unity it is not at all clear as to how. What is the "I" anyway? The nature, origins, correlates, and functions of this unity needed to be studied. Stern himself seemed to suggest that one clue to the *unitas multiplex* came from the goal-directed actions of the subject. Purposive action definitely was registered in subjectivity and could even be said to orient subjectivity in some ways. Stern suggested that autotelic goals are an individual's personal objectives, while heterotelic goals are goals that extend beyond the self and help the individual grow. Syntelic goals are shared with others. Hypertelic goals involve the incorporation of transpersonal goals (e.g. toward God) into the individual's autotelic system.

Stern died in 1938 in the United States after fleeing the Nazis in Germany. His intuition that goals offer a clue concerning the *unitas multiplex* was followed up on by Allport. Gordon Allport appreciated the work Stern had done and tried to carry it forward in the new discipline of personality psychology in the United States.

Gordon Allport (1897–1967) was a psychologist at Harvard University whose main focus of study was personality. Among his many accomplishments was a long struggle within the field of psychology to get psychologists to adopt idiographic methods in their approaches to personality. While this effort failed Allport nonetheless managed to advance personology in many areas but I will discuss only the issue of the origins and grounds of unity or Stern's *unitas multiplex*. Like Stern, Allport invested considerable effort into the question of where the person's unity comes from. What is its ground? His answer was "all the regions (of our personality—P.M.) that we regard as peculiarly ours..." constitute the person's unity (P.M.) "....and which for the time being I suggest we call the proprium..."[45] Thus, it appears that for Allport unity was the result of a kind of decision or cognitive process that identifies some internal content as uniquely mine and no-one else's. It appears to be a kind of interior selection or decision which stipulates that "this material is mine and no-one else knows of it.... or could know it unless I shared it with others". This internal content could involve everything from bodily processes, sufferings, the occasional extension of "mine" to styles, objects or places, desires, values, etc. The point is that the proprium is derived from a cognitive-emotional comparison process that designates one sector of world "mine" and other sectors of the world as not-mine. What kind of cognitive-emotional comparison process would yield the kind of unity characteristic of persons? One candidate of course is agency as understood as a kind of selection process or deliberative decision-making intellectual process. Agency exhibits preferences in terms of what things to preserve, choose, grasp, create, etc. and therefore it is a value orientation and it can give or accept gifts from others.

Despite Allport's pioneering work on the proprium, mainstream psychology did not follow up on the idea. Nevertheless, there were many distinguished psychologists who were not personalists (e.g. Freud, other psychoanalysts, Erickson) who nonetheless creatively used idiographic (mainly narrative) techniques to study persons. In addition many psychologists and philosophers have pointed to the fact that lives appeared to be structured in a story-like manner and that the story may be one way in which people build a unified sense of self—not to mention meaning in their lives.[46,47,48,49,50,51] Henry Murray—a successor to Allport at Harvard—developed and used a number of narrative-based approaches for study of persons.

Narrative is central to personalism both as a phenomenon in itself and as a method of inquiry into persons. When we engage in narrative thinking about ourselves we conceive our lives as a kind of story with a beginning; a middle; and a future, including an ending. Producing a narrative is producing a simulation or a possible world with which we can cognize or bring to life various possibilities that matter to us. Narrative cognition involves model or world building such that we can use these possible worlds to make sense of our lives. Narratives allow us to explore many possible worlds that are alike enough to our world that we can learn something about this world by comparing it to other worlds. To use narrative to derive meaning in my life I need to construct a simulation or model or possible world that obeys laws of narrative coherence and then compare my current self and history with that narrative simulation. Given that persons are composed of both persisting and transient processes, i.e. that persons are inherently temporal, it appears that narrative is the natural mode or cognitive-linguistic domain to capture personal experience. The claim here however is that narrative thinking may be used by persons to confer unity on their experiences, their lives. Narratives have beginnings, middles, climaxes, and ends just as person's lives do. In addition, narratives are composed of characters, roles, scenes, scripts, plots, and the like just as person's lives are. If we can model our lives in terms of narrative coherence then commitment to that narrative model should elicit the sense of unity of consciousness or personality as the narrative model would confer a single meaning on the person's life. In short narrative may be a mode of thinking used by persons to impose a coherent unity on the flux of their experiences and to conceive or construct a kind of unity in their overall life experience.

Murray (1893–1988) was the first psychologist to use narrative inquiry to look at the complete life cycle in order to get an adequate picture of persons. He originated the use of the term personology and developed with his wife the Thematic Apperception Test[52] wherein individuals would observe ink stain like figures and then describe what they thought they saw in the figures. Standardized criteria were used to analyze people's responses and to develop resultant personality profiles of respondents. Murray was also very interested in the author of *Moby Dick*, Herman Melville. By analyzing Melville's biographies as well as his creative works Murray argued that Melville's creative works mirrored the instability of his private emotional life and that Melville used his creative work to treat depression and a temptation to suicide. In a sense Melville used his novels to create a coherent life story for himself. Murray used concepts such as "thema" and "unitythema" to capture persisting emotional needs in Melville's life and these concepts can be used profitably within a life-historical framework.

Other psychologists have taken up Murray's lead in use of narrative techniques to study individual lives. Erik Erikson (1902–1994) wrote life cycle accounts of historical figures such as Luther, Gandhi, Freud, Gorky, Hitler, Jefferson, and others. Erikson tended to view his subjects in terms of his developmental theory of personality change that involves an identity crisis in early maturity and a challenge to generativity versus despair in older age. In McAdams's[53,54,55] work persons are interviewed concerning "chapters" in their lives and then the interviews are coded in narrative terms with some codes capturing a redemptive motif wherein the individual recovers from and flourishes after a crisis of some kind. McAdams has also examined the *unitas multiplex* issue first identified by Stern (though McAdams does not use Stern's terms). McAdams for example looked at how the multiple characters that are aspects of the self are integrated into a single life story. He identified contrasting motives of need for "agency" versus "communion". Unification of the self appears to involve at least in part attempts at integration of these contrasting needs. The agency-communion distinction points to the personalist understanding of persons as unities that oscillate between an immanent pole and a transcendent pole. The agency-communion tension, so highlighted by McAdams is a theme that runs throughout the entire personalist literature as we will see.

The theory of the "dialogical self"[56,57] takes these contrasting motives as almost literal subselves of the individual—little "I"s that compete and conflict with one another in an incessant internal dialog. Unification of self requires cooperation among these little selves rather than one dominant self commanding all other subselves. How to achieve that cooperation that leads to unity? Hermans and Kempen suggest that there are distinct "I" positions capable of becoming the authorial voice that can elicit cooperation from each of the "me's" or subselves. Persons can be interviewed or queried about these subselves and then encouraged or assisted in conducting internal dialogues between each discursive I position and all the others. An interviewee can be asked to imagine that each subself is given a voice and a character in a story or movie and then to observe how the movie unfolds. The authorial voice seeks to attain conversation, consensus, and dialog around a challenge the individual is facing and thus unity is achieved.

While early scientific psychology consolidated narrative approaches to the study of personality, more recent scientific approaches to personality have attempted to understand the unity problem by studying apparent breakdown patterns in unity. Psychiatry and clinical psychology have largely concerned themselves with charting and studying breakdown patterns of the unified person into the divided self. Take for example, the phenomena of akrasia or weakness of will, displayed by most of us on a daily basis and in an extreme fashion by the addict with regard to her drug. Akrasia has been modeled as conflict between two subselves: a current self and the future self. People have a tendency to identify with the impulsive current self—even though doing so will adversely affect the individual in the future. For example, people will choose the chocolate cake NOW even though they know they will regret the choice when they put on more pounds in the future. People have a tendency to think of the future self as a different self in conflict with the present self, making working toward future goals difficult. The conflict between current and future selves has been studied with many methods. A key finding is that to the extent to which you perceive that your present self to be continuous with a future self, you will save more money. If you do not identify with a future ideal self at all you are less likely to save for retirement or anything else. Higher present/future self-continuity predicts reduced discounting of future rewards in a laboratory task, and greater lifetime accumulation of financial assets (even after controlling for age and education). The more individuals resolve the conflict between current and future self the better the ability to plan and save for the future.

Apparent breakdown in the sense of unity occurs in many neuropsychiatric disorders. Some forms of schizophrenia, for example, involve a set of alien thoughts controlling the thoughts and behavior of the individual. Bipolar disorder involves two contrasting personalities and thought patterns. Dissociative identity disorder involves two contrasting personalities vying for control over the behavior of the individual. There are several personality disorders (e.g. borderline, narcissistic, sociopathic) that involve an absence of some elements of the personal in the context of fully functional cognitive capacities.

Within the realms of experimental psychology and neuroscience two recent research programs illustrate some personological approaches to scientific study of apparent breakdown patterns in personal subjectivity. Martin, Sugarman, and Hickinbottom (2010)[58] in experimental social psychology and Price and Barrell (2012)[59] in neuroscience have taken personal subjectivity seriously, respecting its phenomenal attributes as facts and attempting to elucidate its nature, correlates, breakdown patterns, and functions using a wide variety of methodological approaches. Martin et al. define the person as an identifiable, embodied individual human with being, self-understanding, and agentic capability (Martin et al., 2010; p. 27). "Identifiable" refers to the fact that persons carry social identities that mark them off as members of classes or groups, but it is recognized that these identifiers do not exhaust an individual's identity. "Being" refers to existence of a single individual in a cultural life-world. "Self" in self-understanding does not refer to a substantival entity or homunculus in the mind. Self is understood by Martin et al. as a particular kind of understanding—a comprehension of one's unique existence that imbues individual experience and actions with meaning and a sense of being present here and now (Martin et al., p. 28). Personhood therefore is an accomplishment rather than a substance. It is a derivation of meaning out of personal experiences. That ability to derive meaning from experiences can vary, can be more or less successful. When it is not successful we see suffering and psychiatric disorder.

The ability to derive meaning from experiences has recently been fruitfully studied under the so-called predictive processing framework (PPF). For the PPF the brain is essentially a prediction and simulation machine. It specializes in production of expectancies and then processes error signals when those expectancies are not met. All forms of experiences fundamentally derive from these anticipatory simulations (Brightman's shining present) and the resultant error signals. The error signals trigger what is most essential to human persons: meaning-seeking. A human person is an interpretative hybrid that is more akin to an ethical process or activity rather than a substance. It is possible to have persisting sameness of identity over time while still undergoing change. One way to accomplish persistence of identity over time is via a backward-looking process of extraction of meaning from experiences and then attribution of those meanings to a narrative self. The cumulative autobiographical narrative connects strands of meaning from each iteration of the (self-) interpretative process, thus creating a persistent identity across time. But who does this interpretative work? Who is able to range freely over the life experiences of the individual? The agent himself or that agentic process which is the core of the personality.

Price and Barrell (2012) point out that we need to begin with first-person experiences if we are to understand people as agentic or strategic interpreters of their own and others' experiences. All kinds of methods are useful for the study of first-person experiences and perspective, including classic introspection, neuropsychological study of breakdown patterns, phenomenology, experiential sampling methods, diary methods, psychophysical judgment tasks, and neuroimaging, including in-depth studies of the associations of the default mode network (DMN) activation pattern. Old worries about the veridicality and dependability of first-person reports have been ameliorated by showing that one can train participants to be disciplined observers and reporters of their own experiential states.

In addition, unbiased methods of sampling phenomenal experience have been developed as well. One example of these sampling procedures is the descriptive experience sampling procedures where participants carry around with them a beeper which goes off according to a randomized schedule. Participants are trained to observe in an unbiased manner whatever experiences are occurring to them at the time of the beep and to report those experiences in detail. They might audio record the experience into a smartphone and upload it up to the experimenter's Labsite for analysis. These reports of experiences can then be analyzed in multiple ways for themes, structures, emotions, moods, thoughts, and so forth. In longitudinal variants of this method participants meet with the experimenter within 24 hours of reporting an experience to be interviewed in depth about the experience. The process is then repeated over a two-week period, so participants improve in their observations and reporting skills. In short, subjectivity, first-person perspective experiences, as well as the meaning-development process are amenable to scientific study with all of the above personalistically inspired methods.

Summary

Our survey of previous personalisms has turned up some relevant ideas for a new eschatological personalism. The theme of the agentic experience as being the core fundamental basis of the unity experience in consciousness, and the agentic future-oriented thinking and feeling was important given eschtatology's rootedness in the future. Some previous personalists emphasized that unity in consciousness was also linked to striving for ethical ideals—a future-oriented stance. The PPF treats the brain essentially as an agentic prediction machine made to create forecasts of future dangers and opportunities. Every level of the neural hierarchy operates to create simulations of anticipated realities that are compared to current sensory evidence and then adjusted to minimize error in the next cycle in order to meet the ideal specified in the predictive simulation and so forth. Personality involves a seeking after meaning and value with ethical striving the logical outcome of value-seeking. Ethical striving to attain some ideal self is therefore deeply rooted in our neurobiology.

Although I do not think previous thinkers have given us a clear explanation as to how unity of consciousness works, they at least identified its importance for an eschatological personalism. Its importance lies in the fact that the experience of unity is indivisible, unlike all other objects in the universe. It is therefore a candidate for the basic essence of personality. Subjectivity is the feeling of what it is like to be me. It involves first-person perspective and unity of consciousness. It involves feelings, qualia, cognitions, and temporality. Brightman gave us a very rich description of its structure when he described the shining present and illuminating absent. A key activity of subjectivity is meaning-seeking—another commonly discussed theme in previous personalisms. We not only undergo experiences we seek to interpret them. Every experience we undergo is subject to interpretation by the agent and this gives the subject freedom to distance himself from his experiences. He rises above anything that happens to him as he chooses how to interpret those happenings.

Surprisingly solitude was another frequent theme discussed by personalists. For some solitude allowed one to re-establish a "thou" relation to Nature—in opposition to the machine which knew only how to dominate nature. Solitude also was conceived as a primordial condition of human beings and thus a necessary process for nurturance of personality in opposition to the crowd.

Subjectivity involves an activity, an oscillation between an interiorly focused immanence and exteriorly focused transcendence. Love is the process that unifies the two poles into one experience. Love is conceived as an ecstatic moving outside of oneself to encounter and value what is most unique in the Other. It is the faculty that can perceive personality. When it does it sees what is noblest and best in that person and reverences that value while loving the person warts and all. It picks out the personal and thus it contains the secret to the personal.

Notes

1 Bengtsson, Jan Olof. *The worldview of personalism: Origins and early development.* Oxford: Oxford University Press, 2006. While Bengtsson does not discuss intellectual precursors to the development of 19th-century personalism it is worth mentioning some of those precursors here. Substantial personalist themes abounded within the primordial religious traditions associated with shamanic practices (e.g. in the circumpolar, American, and African regions) as well as within those traditions that emphasized the "sacred Kingship" (which was a virtually universal phenomena across the world up until the modern era; see McNamara, Patrick. *Spirit possession and history: History, psychology, and neurobiology.* Westford, CT: ABC-CLIO, 2011).

At the very opening of the Western tradition, we find Heraclitus noting that the soul or subjectivity is so complex, deep, and mysterious that it is near impossible to explicate its nature, ordering principle, or logos (DK22B45).

Plato's teacher and Athenian gadfly Socrates evidenced a number of positions consistent with personalism, such as belief in an immortal component of the human psyche/self/soul (for example, Socrates was frequently seen consulting with his personal daemon…an intrapsychic voice that would only tell him what NOT to do rather than what to do), the capital importance of what we today would call conscience and the frank admittance of one's own ignorance concerning eternal truths.

While Plato in the *Symposium* pointed to love as humanity's true nature and placed the individual who loves midway between the perishable and the eternal, Plato also tended to place the destiny of the soul away from this world and into the realm of the eternal ideas. This world was likened to a cave and individuals to prisoners in the cave who attempted to discern reality by watching shadows cast by a fire onto the cave wall. Philosophy was a way out of the cave and into the blazing daylight of reality.

Aristotle's hylomorphic theory of individuality asserts that a kind of proto-matter individuates human beings via the soul's form informing the proto-matter, which, in turn, is considered to emerge from potentiality in order to be informed by soul. Aristotle's other contribution to personalism however comes in the form of his virtue ethics. He notes, like Confucius in China, that personal character is created via cultivation of the emotions and virtues. Personhood is not possible without cultivation of the virtues. This is because human beings come equipped with conflicting emotional dispositions that need to be fine-tuned to the local culture and that need to be transformed so that they are not focused on immediate gratification of desire but instead serve long term flourishing of self and others. Prudence (and what would later be called synderesis or conscience by philosophers in the Middle Ages) orchestrates appropriate deployment of virtuous behaviors in service to self and others.

Consistent with the autarchy developed in this book, the Greek and Roman cynics and stoics emphasized attempts to keep oneself free despite the surrounding political tyrannies. Even if one is thrown in jail one is not ultimately harmed because individual conscience cannot be compelled. Diogenes, for example, emphasized complete freedom of action for the self and cultivation of indifference to surrounding cultural norms. Epictetus argued that no one can be enslaved or harmed if one insists on maintaining personal integrity and indifference to the winds of fortune.

Just as in the East, insights into the nature of the Self in the West were propelled forward by both religious thinkers and the philosophers. Eastern religions texts and practices must be considered key sources of personalist insights in the modern era. The so-called "divine" kings all over the world and across the entire ancient period created models of sovereign individuality. In the Near East, the institution of the divine kingship was strong in Egypt but less so in Mesopotamia and Israel. Nevertheless, even in ancient Israel the Davidic Kingship incorporated some elements of divine kingship as seen in the Davidic psalms some of which express a very highly developed sense of self and interiority, a relation with a personal God and an exalted sense of the personal dignity of the self in relation to God. This God is personal through and through. He enters into voluntary covenants with whom he will. When Moses asks him who he is he answers "I will be who I will be" (Ex. 3:13–14) that is I am a definite being but I define myself. No-one else can define who I am. God reveals himself to Job and it is this revelation of himself as person that finally provides an answer to Job's distress. The Hebrew prophets also presented models of fearless and highly individuated persons called forth by personal vocations that defined personality for these individuals.

The advent of Christianity brought the issue of the person front and center. Love, personality's defining attribute, is given a central role in both the divinity and human life in the New Testament. When St Paul complains (Romans 7:15), "For that which I do I know not: for what I would, that do I not; but what I hate, that do I", he perfectly highlights the inner conflict that is so central an experience of the self. Only putting on the mind of Christ will heal the inner conflict of self with self in order to build the personal.

Attempts to understand the nature of the Christ—the God-man Jesus—with Greek philosophical categories began in the New Testament with John identifying the person Jesus with the logos or the ordering principle of the cosmos. This is a key personalist claim—that a person or the personal logos are the key to the nature of the cosmos. Religiously motivated discussions of the nature of the person however climaxed some three and half centuries later in the debates at the great ecumenical councils such as the First Council of Nicaea (325) and the First Council of Constantinople (381). The Church fathers had to formulate a coherent story as to how the person of Jesus could contain two natures (divine and human) without fracturing his unified sense of self. The other major mystery was how you could have one God with three distinct "persons". The solution tended to emphasize relations rather than substances marking the distinctions (the Father eternally "begets" the Son and the two eternally generate the Spirit, etc.).

Another Church father, St Augustine, presented several arguments that emphasized a turn toward inwardness in the search for truth and a sophisticated analysis of the major components of the person such as rationality, Will, freedom, desire, and love. The Christian emphasis on Love as a key to understanding the nature of the person is consistent with other religious approaches to the self found in the East (where compassion, benevolence, and mercy toward others are emphasized).

Although the early Christian emphasis on love was never forgotten, Boethius (ca. 480–524) argued that a person was characterized not by love, per se but instead was more precisely characterized as an individual substance of a rational nature ("persona est naturae rationalis individua substantia").

The great monastic communities founded across the Christian world during the pre-modern period (particularly in Ireland) nurtured a deep interior sense and intense personal relation with the personal deity. The monks emphasized silence, solitude, personal vocation/destiny, humility, love of self, God and other, communal relations, examination of personal conscience (again particularly the Irish monks), and speculative learning—all fundamental virtues of the personalist stance. The medieval philosophers would generally follow Boethius' definition of the person as a rational being but add to it the Christian virtues including love as a central defining feature of the person.

While the Muslim philosopher Averroes tended to assimilate the individual into the divine by arguing that individually illumined intellects were mere instances of the divine mind, St Thomas Aquinas gave greater weight to the individual by presenting a detailed model concerning the way in which Love informed the free will and the agent intellect during action planning and knowledge acquisition. Interestingly, although Aristotle did not emphasize the agent intellect in his "On the soul" the Muslim and Christian Aristotelians took the idea very seriously and treated it as central to personhood—a stance quite consistent with the eschatological personalism developed here. After all, agency is crucial for action and choice, and therefore to freedom of the will. Despite the error of voluntarism associated with their moral philosophies, the nominalists, in their attempts to deny reality to universals helped to focus attention on concrete particulars and individuals.

The immense weight placed by thinkers such as Duns Scotus and William of Ockham on human freedom as manifested in the individual before God signaled the rise of the individual as a special focus of philosophical inquiry during the modern period.

The great Renaissance humanists, such as Nicholas Cusanus, Petrarch (who wrote a much neglected essay on the relation of solitude to contemplation and creativity), and Pico Della Mirandola, placed the issue of the special dignity of man front and center on the philosophical table. Cusanus (Nicholas of Cusa) adumbrated his idea of the individual as a union of opposites and of God too as a union of opposites. The individual is characterized by both the personal and the impersonal, the finite and the infinite, and the two imply one another. Finiteness would have no meaning if we could not compare it to the idea of the infinite. God too is characterized by both the unconditioned and the conditioned. He incarnates so that the individual human being can become deified.

The two remain separate. God is not man and man is not God. Within the unity of the God-man relationship there is one movement composed of two moments encompassing an ascending infinite (deification) and a descending infinite (incarnation). The multiplicity or plurality of individuals manifests the One, or God's creativity and glory, just as the indivisible One is contained within each individual.

The Cusanus-inspired personalist conception of the coincidence of opposites requires a new logic that, while upholding the hard won insights of the Aristotelian syllogisms, moves beyond Aristotle's law of the excluded middle in order to account for the manifest facts of complex wholes that contain phenomenal opposites, the coincidence of opposites. Many modern non-classical logics like paraconsistent and modal logics can accommodate Cusanus' insights. What appeared as irresolvable paradox from the point of view of classical logic is grasped as essential fact from the point of view of these newer logics (see for example, Priest, Grahman. "*One: Being an investigation into the unity of reality and of its parts, including the singular object which is nothingness.* Oxford: Oxford University Press, 2014).

Like 20th-century personalist thinkers (such as Nikolai Berdyaev and Peter Bertocci), Pico located human dignity in the creativity of the person. Montaigne (who also wrote an essay on solitude) argued that tolerance for others and the phenomena of friendship were the relations that were characteristic of the personal.

Philosophers of the Modern period, such as Gottfried Leibniz, Rene Descartes, John Locke, Thomas Reid, and culminating especially with Immanuel Kant, integrated insights of the medievals and those developed by the Renaissance thinkers concerning man as the measure of all things and reasserted the special and inviolable dignity of the individual human being. An individual cannot be treated as a means to an end but instead has infinite intrinsic worth grounded in his personhood. Individuality/personhood contains within it an infinite content or complete thought (Leibniz); its indissoluble unity includes its rationality (Descartes), its memory (Locke), and its freedom (Reid).

2 Stitskin, Leon D. *Jewish philosophy: A study in personalism.* Brooklyn, NY: Yeshiva University Press, 1976.

3 Norton, David. *Personal destinies. A philosophy of ethical individualism.* Princeton, NJ: Princeton University Press, 1976.

4 For a succinct overview of the intellectual antecedents and current trends in personalist thought see the excellent entry in the *Stanford Encyclopedia of Philosophy* by Thomas Woods and Olaf Bengtsson "Personalism" 2018) https://plato.stanford.edu/entries/personalism/ 07.27.19

5 Stirner, Max. *Stirner: The ego and its own.* Cambridge: Cambridge University Press, 1995.

6 Bakunin, Michael. *God and the state.* New York: Courier Corporation, 2012.

7 Quoted in Hellman, John. *Emmanuel Mounier: The new Catholic left 1930–1950.* Buffalo, NY: University of Toronto Press, 1981.

8 Berdayaev, Nikolaï. *The meaning of history.* New York: Meridian Books, 1936/1962.

9 See, for example, his *Oneself as another,* trans. Kathleen Blamey, Chicago, IL: University of Chicago Press, 1992 (1990).

10 Gracia. J. Individuality: An essay on the foundations of metaphysics. Buffalo, NY: SUNY Press, 1988

11 Crosby, John F. *The selfhood of the human person.* Washington, DC: CUA Press, 1996.

12 "Theory of Man," by Francisco Romero, trans. William F. Cooper (1966).

13 Bowne, Borden Parker. *Personalism*. Boston, MA and New York: Houghton, Mifflin, 1908.
14 Bowne, Borden Parker. *Metaphysics*. New York: American Book Company, 1898, p. 63.
15 Bowne, Borden Parker. *Personalism*. Boston, MA and New York: Houghton, Mifflin, 1908, pp. 199–100.
16 Auxier, Randall. *Time will and purpose: Living ideas in the philosophy of Josiah Royce*. New York: Open Court Press, 2013.
17 Flewelling, Ralph Tyler, ed. *The personalist*. Vol. 3. Los Angeles, CA: School of Philosophy, University of Southern California, 1922.
18 Flewelling, Ralph Tyler. *Personalism and the problems of philosophy: An appreciation of the work of Borden Parker Bow*ne. New York and Cincinnati: Methodist Book Concern, 1915.
19 Knudson, Albert C. *The philosophy of personalism*. New York and Cinncinatti: The Abingdon Press, 1927.
20 Bertocci, Peter Anthony, and Richard M. Millard. *Personality and the good: Psychological and ethical perspectives*. New York: David McKay Co., 1963.
21 *Religion as creative insecurity*, by Peter A. Bertocci. New York: Association Press, 1958.
22 Bertocci, Peter A. *Sex, love, and the person*. New York: Sheed and Ward, 1967.
23 Bertocci, Peter A. *The person God is*. London: Routledge, 2013, first published 1970.
24 See Bertocci, 1970, 43–45.
25 King Jr, Martin Luther. *Stride toward freedom: The Montgomery story*. Vol. 1. Boston, MA: Beacon Press, 2010. 100.
26 See also Burrow, 1999, 287–293; this generational account of the Boston personalist tradition is largely based on Burrow's history.
27 Kohak, Erazim. *The embers and the stars*. Chicago, IL: University of Chicago Press, 1987.
28 Kohak also wrote a beautiful reminiscence of the personalist tradition at Boston University (BU) that can still be read at www.bu.edu/philo/people/alumni/ (June 6, 2017).
29 Muelder, Walter George. *The ethical edge of Christian theology: Forty years of communitarian personalism*. New York: Edwin Mellen Press, 1983.
30 Brightman, Edgar Sheffield. Personality as a metaphysical principle, In *Personalism in theology* (pp. 40–63). Boston: Boston University Press, 1943. 56.
31 Brightman, 1943, 55.
32 Brightman, 1943, 55–56.
33 see Brightmann, 1943, 57–60.
34 Brightman, Edgar Sheffield. *Person and reality*. New York: Ronald Press Co., 1958.
35 In reviewing Brightman's papers at the Gotlieb Archival Center at Boston University I discovered that Newhall also appeared to be working on a collection of papers from a variety of scholars on Brightman's work. As far as I know this festschrift for Brightman never appeared.
36 Brightman, 1958, 35–36.
37 Brightman, 1958, 40.
38 Brightmann, 1958, 56.
39 Brightman, 1958, 107.
40 Brightman, 1958, 121.
41 Brightman 1958, 268.
42 Lamiell, James T. *Beyond individual and group differences: Human individuality, scientific psychology, and William Stern's critical personalism*. Thousand Oaks, CA: Sage Publications, 2003.

43 Lamiell, 2003, 38.
44 Windelband, Wilhelm. History and natural science. *Theory & Psychology*, 8 1998: 5–22 (original work published 1904, p. 13).
45 Allport, Gordon Willard. *Becoming; Basic considerations for a psychology of personality*. New Haven, CT: Yale University Press, 1955. 40.
46 Bruner, Jerome S. *Acts of meaning*. Cambridge, MA: Harvard University Press, 1990.
47 Bruner, Jerome S., and Jerome S. Bruner. *Actual minds, possible worlds*. Cambridge, MA: Harvard University Press, 2009.
48 Carr, David. *Time, narrative, and history*. Bloomington: Indiana University Press, 1986.
49 MacIntyre, Alasdair. *After virtue*. Vol. 99. Notre Dame: University of Notre Dame Press, 1984.
50 Ricoeur, Paul. "*Time and narrative*, Vol. I." trans. K. McLaughlin and D. Pellauer. Chicago, IL: University of Chicago Press, 1984.
51 Sarbin, Theodore R. *Narrative psychology: The storied nature of human conduct*. Westport, CT: Praeger Publishers/Greenwood Publishing Group, 1986.
52 Murray, Henry Alexander, and Edwin S. Shneidman. *Endeavors in psychology: Selections from the personology of Henry A. Murray*. New York: HarperCollins Publishers, 1981.
53 McAdams, Dan P. *Power, intimacy, and the life story: Personological inquiries into identity*. New York: Guilford Press, 1988.
54 McAdams, Dan P. "Unity and purpose in human lives: The emergence of identity as a life story." In A. I. Rabin, R. A. Zucker, R. A. Emmons, & S. Frank (Eds.), Studying persons and lives (pp. 148–200). New York: Springer Publishing Co., 1990.
55 McAdams, Dan P. *The person: An introduction to personality psychology*. San Diego, CA: Harcourt Brace Jovanovich, 1990.
56 Hermans, Hubert J. M, and Harry J. G Kempen. *The dialogical self: Meaning as movement*. San Diego, CA: Academic Press, 1993.
57 Hermans, Hubert J., Harry J. Kempen, and Rens J. Van Loon. "The dialogical self: Beyond individualism and rationalism." *American Psychologist* 47.1 (1992): 23.
58 Martin, J., Jeff H. Sugarman, and Sarah. Hickinbottom. *Persons: Understanding psychological selfhood and agency*. London: Springer, 2010.
59 Price, Donald, and James Barrell. *Inner experience and neuroscience: Merging both perspectives*. Cambridge, MA: MIT Press Bradford Books, 2012.

3   Possible worlds and the agent intellect

We discussed the need for a new form of personalism—one that could meet the demands of the coming new age of globalized technocracies, intelligent machines, ecological crises, and even potentially becoming a multi-planet species. We briefly surveyed the works of previous personalist thinkers and identified several elements that an eschatological personalism would benefit from, including an account of the origins and metaphysical status of person-hood; an account of the unity of consciousness based on agency or the agent intellect; an account of the nature and structure of subjectivity; and the role that meaning, value-seeking, and love plays in constituting persons. What was missing from these previous personalisms was an awareness of the eschatological age we now find ourselves in, a consistent account of autarchy or the self-rule (which follows logically from the grounding of personhood in the agent intellect; see below), a personalist philosophy of technology, and an account of the relation of that sovereign individual to the state and the rise of the intelligent machines. A new personalism most importantly would require some explication of the metaphysical and theological basis for the assertion that the personal is the key to all reality and is the ultimate value.

Persons although created by God are not "caused" by God

I will begin with a theological story concerning the personal and the eschaton:

All previous personalisms and all previous theologies of the human person have asserted that because the human person was created by God, the human person was therefore *caused* by God and that this causal effect was the source of the person's dependency on God. The view apparently is that for any created reality x, it is a condition of the possibility of x that there be a cause of x. Given the creaturely status of human persons, it follows according to this line of reasoning that human persons cannot be the cause of themselves—they do not bring themselves into being. They are therefore caused, or determined by some superior force.

But God's creative activity cannot be considered causal activity per se because the activity occurs outside of time and causal effects can occur only in time. Causality is a form of necessity and therefore unfreedom. God's creative activity involves the creation of time itself so causes do not operate "when" creation occurs. This is not a mere semantic distinction. Divine power and creativity are not the same as "causing". Causing is deterministic while God's actions are inherently creative and free. Creativity implies that something novel is brought into Being or is revealed. Genuinely new things are not caused in any traditional sense. New things were not embedded in any relations "before" they were revealed or brought into Being, so they cannot have been caused in any traditional sense. The idea that persons are "caused" furthermore is not consistent with the fact that we are free in our cognitions, willing activities, and creative activities. We cannot be free and be caused at the same time.

Being created by God as free beings with real autonomy such that our actions matter does not diminish the fact that we are also utterly dependent upon God. Indeed, it can be argued that our freedom intensifies that dependency because we are free to (put it bluntly) screw things up. In addition, from a Christian eschatological point of view, we as "persons" are immortal. That means that while it appears that we are not self-sustaining, that we will die and all that we love will pass away, that is only appearance and illusion for those whose "robes", in the words of the *Book of Revelation*, have been washed in the blood of the Lamb. For orthodox Christians, "persons" will rise in a new bodily form with the resurrection of the dead at the Second Coming. That is a bedrock, ontological fact for believing Christians and it is consistent with the claim here that standard deterministic causation does not occur with the creation and ultimate destiny of human persons.

God calls us out of possibility into existence or actuality and offers the gift of existence (in the form of friendship with God) to us. Note that unlike the rest of creation, persons are not created ex nihilo; they are, instead, created from out of the realm of possibility, i.e. the Mind of God. Persons were ideas in the Mind of God before they were brought into actuality by God. The ideas of God are not the same as his essence or actuality. There is some real distinction between God and his ideas. God is pure, everlasting, generative, actuality that is overflowing with creativity. His "ideas" concern that part of his activity that is "Othering" or kenotic. God is Love and is constantly emptying out his Self into "Others", into possibilities. This "Othering" creates real ontological distinctions between God's ideas and God's Self and between God's creatures and God.

When God seeks to give himself to an individual person, that "idea" becomes manifest via the individual coming into existence. The individual is granted real independent existence apart from God so that God can give himself fully to that individual. The individual is free because he is real or is real because he is free to accept or decline God's gift. Some immediately accept the gift and live in a blissful state of collaborative union with God. Others of us immediately reject the offer/gift and are immediately sent back into potentiality or into "idea" status. Still others (most of us, in fact) accept the gift and begin a collaboration with God, but then decide later to go it alone and create something without God's collaboration (i.e. to rival God). But since our full reality depends on that collaboration, the "go it alone" strategy fails. That failure carries with it consequences for the "actuality" we experience as persons that I will discuss below.

To make us real beings, capable of real consent to friendship with God, He made us Beings with some measure of autonomy and real standing in the universe. That autonomy is realized in the way we govern ourselves. We own ourselves and are responsible for our actions. We are free. Our self-rule/autarchy, however, is the result of two wills, God and ourselves. As many of the classical personalist philosophers argued, God who is, in essence free, generous act, calls us to a particular vocation or destiny that constitutes our very identity and our very selves. We cannot realize our freedom without contact with the source of freedom, God. We lose our self-rule when we lose contact with God. When we go it alone we make ourselves vulnerable to all kinds of non-freedoms or forms of slavery. Our selves become divided, as self-rule is no longer possible.

The ones who chose to reject partnership with God and "go it alone" were our ancestors Adam and Eve and their descendants. The "go it alon-ers" create a third ontological realm where they interpose their creations between themselves and Nature. The first realm is God or pure free creative activity. The second realm is the collaboration between God and Man, i.e. Nature and the Kingdom of God. And the third realm created by the "go it aloners" is called TIME, and it is composed of us, fallen nature, and the machines. We "go it aloners" are in a liminal state: neither fully real in timeless friendship with God, nor a complete nothing-ness.

God's call consists principally of instilling the capacity for free activity/ creativity to create or realize worlds or ideas that are unique to each of us, infused with God/freedom and that contains the seed of that individual's destiny and complete fulfillment and happiness. The call also contains an imperative for the individual to realize his or her unique idea or destiny— an idea that only a collaboration with God can realize. God's call also immerses us in a sea of possibilities as the call is to a collaborative creativity with God and this is called freedom. We awaken and are thrown into a sea of free possibilities, so it is no wonder that there is a temptation to linger and consider the options or to see what you can create on your own. But those possibilities are merely a reflection of the freedom that characterizes our existential situation when we are called. We are being asked to be co-creators of the universe so it is fitting that we are created free or immersed in a realm of "possibilities".

Once we reject the collaboration with God those possibilities are experienced as Time or more specifically the "future" (what might be). Those possibilities however are distorted if we see them from the realm of TIME instead of seeing them from the eternal realm of God's Kingdom. Real creativity is only possible via co-creativity with God. But before we can be these co-creators we have to say Yes, we have to consent to the collaboration. We are free to accept the gift or to deny it. Within the realm of Time where there is an attempt to exclude God, we attempt to go it alone by acting like God: we attempt to create new worlds. If we attempt to bring some possibilities into the realm of the actual we only end-up bringing them into this in-between or liminal realm of Time (our realm). Thus, the things we create (including machines) will "exist" only liminally—neither fully real nor mere nothingness. Their powers will be liminal (subject to entropy) as well. All of our creations are subjected to futility as they will have this liminal quality if we create without God. Our attempts to create without God are the sin of pride or hubris referenced in Genesis. It is characteristic of the liminal state. It is not merely "going it alone". It is an attempt to be a sole creator. Thus, all our creations will be products of time-bound, liminal human creativity.

Even though our creations will be time-bound, some realizations of possibilities will be wonderful for human beings (though still ultimately futile as all things are condemned to pass away in time), but many will be monstrous and this is the origin of suffering and evil. We can end that suffering and evil by accepting God's invitation to collaborate. However, we seem stuck in time, enslaved to various anesthetics that help us to forget the dizzying effects of freedom and responsibility or autarchy. When we reject God's offer, we reject authentic self-rule. When we do not have self-rule it is difficult to say Yes to God or to commit to anyone at all and accept responsibility for our free activity and choices.

To destroy the lethargy and slavery we find ourselves in when trapped in Time, and to pull us out of the in-between realm of liminality, God decides to break into Time and enter the in-between state as well. This is called the incarnation of Christ. The incarnation heightens the eschatological age which began with Zoroaster as it realizes the first fruits of the Kingdom of God. Although we are still in the liminal realm, we are now *en route* to the Kingdom of God. Or better, we can now realize some of those first fruits of the Kingdom if we can now and then (as the Buddhists say) "wake up" or participate in the sacramental life of the Church. The incarnation breaks the enchantment of the liminal state by making the liminal state itself the arena for the coming Kingdom of God. For those who choose God, time is destroyed and transfigured into the eternal. This effectively destroys the powers of the monstrous things created within the liminal state that haunt human beings (suffering and death), that keeps us from saying Yes to Life. But it also strengthens and transforms things that enhance human freedom. When God enters the liminal state eternity enters into time and thereby destroys time eschatologically. God destroys the liminal space by destroying the forms of change called suffering and death. They slowly pass away but other things like the products of human creativity (including the arts, science, and technology) acquire potential redemptive powers insofar as they can help us realize the Kingdom of God among us. That is why Christ chose to undergo the cross, to eliminate the liminal "option". As Rudolf Bultmann said, by destroying Time the incarnation ensured that we have nowhere to go but into an eschatological space: the *hour of decision*, i.e. to accept or reject the invitation to collaborate with God. We call this hour of decision or eschatological realm "history". Thus, the need for an eschatological personalism

Those individuals interested in the collaboration with God; interested in realizing manifestations of the transcendentals: the true, the good, and the beautiful; and interested finally in the ideal of autarchy can grasp first fruits of the incarnation including realization of the personal. This sense of the personal I suggest may be a prerequisite for future realization of the resurrection body at the eschaton. Eschatological personalists will cultivate this sense of the personal. Because of the incarnation and participation in a sacramental, ecclesial life, they will experience a new form of temporality; one characterized by some theologians as anticipation and hope—an eschatological temporality. This form of temporality is best captured by the traditional Christian sacraments, ritual and liturgy. The eschatological personalists are pilgrims orientated toward the new Heaven and Earth and engaging in forms of creativity that will realize this new freedom. And so ends this short theological story concerning the new eschatological sense of the personal, creativity and God.

What then do we mean by this new form of the personal?

The personal is a metaphysical ultimate

Persons are basic, ultimate, irreducible entities of reality. They are created by God but not caused by God. If persons were caused by God, they might be considered determined entities and their cause would be "prior to" or more basic or ultimate than they themselves. They could not constitute resurrection bodies as their identities would be dependent on what caused them and therefore would be contingent and ephemeral. Resurrected persons on the other hand are immortal and therefore their identities cannot be ephemeral. Although they would remain creatures, they would nevertheless be immortal, fully embodied persons. As argued above, being created by God is not the same as being caused by God. Causal effects are inherently temporal effects (cause comes before effect, etc.), but God is above, beyond, and outside of clock Time. He may contain or exemplify a perfect form of temporality but he is not subject to Time. Therefore, his actions, including the action of raising the Dead at the eschaton to new life in resurrection bodies, are not causal in the traditional sense. God, as we noted above, is free creative activity. Freedom precludes determinate causing. Free creative activity cannot create unfree, contingent beings. Creation has real autonomy from God. Creation is contingent upon God only in the sense that God's power could end creation at any time if He so willed it. God cannot force a decision upon us. He cannot abrogate free will or the process of consent. Free activity cannot "do" unfree things (that would be tantamount to sin). Freedom creates other freedoms when it creates persons. Creation is gift of God's Self to other Selves. If the gift is rejected then it is either withdrawn or left in a kind of liminal state awaiting reconsideration and acceptance. Persons in the liminal state take on a kind of contingent character in that their selves are divided, with one face turned toward the gift and the other turned away. But persons in their essence (and certainly when resurrected at the end of Time) remain non-contingent beings as they are rooted beyond Time in the free creative activity of God.

Persons in their essence are also simple, without parts. If they had parts those parts would be ultimate rather than the person being ultimate. The simplicity of personhood manifests for us in the experience of agency of consciousness. But agency here must not be thought apart from receptivity and subjectivity. Agency, the personalists have shown, though experienced as a unity in awareness or consciousness nevertheless oscillates between a receptive pole and an agentic pole. That dipolar unity which is agency is not composed of parts but is ceaseless actuality (which is why we call it agency) and therefore experienced paradoxically as an immutable experiential activity. Although persons are "created" they are nevertheless eternal in the sense that they were ideas in the Mind of God when they were called into being and they remain rooted in free creative activity of God. They were not created out of nothingness. Persons are ultimate as no-thing conditions or limits or constrains the free willing of the person. God is also ultimate but He is not a thing, but free activity and free activity does not constrain other freedoms. Nor do other freedoms constrain God in any way. Finally, persons must be self-ruled as nothing can constrain their freedom. Thus, autarchy has a metaphysical basis and is derived directly from the essence of persons.

Persons being simple wholes are also unities. The experience of unity simultaneously expresses a person's uniqueness and confers or establishes that personal uniqueness. Persons experience themselves as unified or one entity. When one just sits quietly and lets the mind wander, the set of impressions that arise are experienced as multifarious, but we nevertheless experience ourselves as a unity. We do not experience a scene or view as a collection of separate objects unless we make an effort to do so. In their treatment of the unity of consciousness Bayne and Chalmers (2003)[1] argue that two experiences are "subsumptively unified" "when they are both subsumed by a single state of consciousness" (p. 27). But the authors are not too clear as to how subsumption occurs. One possibility is that it may be a temporal phenomenon. Two elements are considered subsumed into a single state when they present at the same time, i.e. in the subjective present NOW. In short subsumption would be a kind of time stamp process. Co-occurrence in a particular temporal frame yields unity. A similar kind of time stamp process has been discussed as the process of binding in the neuroscience literature. Binding in the visual modality, for example, is the process of tying various features and objects of a visual scene together into a unified visual experience. The brain accomplishes this feat by co-activation of each area of the brain that handles each of the features that compose the scene. Co-activation is essentially a time stamp process in that activation has to occur simultaneously in the subjective present if the experience is to be unified.

But timing and co-occurrence cannot explain unity of consciousness. There are many things that co-occur in time in my mind that are not associated with a single unified percept. As I type for example, I can experience typing and listening to music as two separate things even though they are occurring simultaneously. Something else is needed to understand the experience of unity. If persons own themselves and their free activity they are ends in themselves and autonomous creative beings in their own right. At the center of this free activity is the creative act of bringing into being from out of the realm of the possible, new worlds, things, and ideas. The creative act of bringing something from a potential state into an actual state is the basis of the felt unity in consciousness and is accomplished by the *agent intellect*. The sense of presence, of being present, of awareness, of suchness, and of being actual and actualizing may be at the basis of the experience of unity and of human moral experience.[2] The sense of being actual derives from the capacity of the agent intellect to bring new things into existence, to actualize things, including one's self. You can directly experience the agent intellect by simply conjuring up something in your imagination. To imagine, model, entertain, manipulate, behold, consider, actualize and reflect upon etc., an image is to utilize the agent intellect. And to do all these things when guided by the transcendentals is to imagine reverently. But the thing or image brought to life –to actuality does not follow from any old actualizing process. It is reliably linked only with the case of bringing instances of the transcendentals into Being. When we bring things into Being that enrich human experience we are more fully real, present, and actual. The sense of agency, of course, is also fundamental to the human experience of intentionality, perspective taking, and feeling personal responsibility for one's actions—all crucial elements of personhood. We can now provide a provisional definition of "person":

A person is a unity and a rational agent who utilizes the agent intellect to know/love Others and to bring into existence ongoing and novel manifestations of the transcendentals, the true, the good, and the beautiful.

Eschatological marks of the personal

An eschatological personalism throws new light on previous philosophical treatments of the nature of persons. Take for example, John Crosby's "The selfhood of the human person".[3] Crosby argues cogently for four central claims regarding marks of the personal or the nature of persons: (1) Persons are ends in themselves. (2) Persons are wholes, not parts. (3) Persons are not instances of some larger genus/species; they are incommunicably their own and unrepeatable. (4) Each person belongs to himself and no other. These four claims were briefly discussed above and are certainly consistent with what I am calling eschatological personalism or autarchy/self-rule. The autarch is a unity, not reducible to something else and not assimilable into something else. He belongs to himself and no other. That is a precondition, along with freedom, of love—the ability to give oneself away fully as gift to another. You cannot give yourself if you do not have, possess, "own", or rule yourself. Autarchy is necessary for sacrificial love.

The Kantian claim that persons are ends in themselves and cannot be used or treated as means to some end is strengthened when seen through eschatological eyes. If the true identity and destiny of the person lie in his or her eschatological free activity and future in a supremely good new Heaven and new Earth, then the value of each individual is anchored beyond Time and is strictly immeasurable/infinite. If identity/destiny is revealed/fulfilled only at history's end, then each person cannot represent or be an instance of any one thing that comes before that end. All such entities will be annihilated at history's end. Why can't a person be a part of some greater whole? As Gracia (1988)[4] argued persons are non-instantiable. Non-instantiability follows from the inherent freedom that IS each person and their anchoring in the "End". As free, persons cannot be constrained, limited, or conditioned by any other thing or freedom. Persons cannot be assimilated into any other entity and remain a person. Because they are simple wholes, they cannot be parts of some other entity or whole. The unity in consciousness testifies to that effect. If a person's essence or nature is not revealed until the End (the Parousia), then his reality, his very self is anchored or rooted in that future eternity and can't be grasped fully or assimilated by anything in the present.

If a person is both indivisible and non-instantiable then he/she is unlike any other "thing" in the universe. He cannot be subdivided into smaller parts and he cannot be assimilated into a larger whole. He is his own "thing" or haecceity. His haecceity is manifested or experienced as unity in consciousness. This individualized existential reality or unity/haecceity implies that personhood is a fundamental fact or reality of the universe.

Claiming that persons are fundamental facts of the universe is a reasonable claim that strengthens eschatological personalism. The neutral monism of Bertrand Russell or the panpsychism of William James demonstrates that the claim that some form of mentality is a basic datum of reality is not fringe philosophy. It has become increasingly recognized by mainstream philosophers and scientists that you cannot derive mentality or consciousness from some kind of emergent process. It has to be there at the start. No bottom-up process will give you mind unless you start with something like mind to begin with. Unfortunately, many of these philosophers cannot allow themselves to take the full personalist position, where not only mental "particles" but also the personal itself are fundamental. Subjectivity in the sense of unity and agency in consciousness is fundamental. Asserting that small particles of mentality or consciousness are part of the basic stuff of the universe does not solve the problem of consciousness as you still have what is called the "combination problem". How do you get subjectivity as we know it, simply by combining a bunch of proto-mental particles? In my view you simply cannot derive consciousness/subjectivity as we know it via any kind of emergent process. Instead, personal consciousness is a fundamental reality.

Certain personalist philosophers have presented arguments for the idea of the personal as fundamental. McTaggart, for example, in his Nature of Existence,[5] argues that the universe is composed fundamentally of selves or persons who are inter-related via love and friendship. There is no traditional God within McTaggart's account. Instead Reality or the whole is composed of indivisible individuals who are inter-related within a community. These individuals are different from one another and in McTaggart's account they also have internal structure which he calls qualities or parts. Note that in McTaggart's account you can have internal structure or qualities/parts but still be simple and indivisible. If there were no differentiated individuals then we would have a featureless, uniform, homogeneous universe—essentially nothingness. But we manifestly have differentiated individuals. But the differentiation is derived from individual's relations—not from internal parts. Differentiated individuals imply relations between these individuals. These relations course through the individual so to speak and link the individuals into a whole which constitutes the fundamental reality. The parts within each individual, in turn, must be understood as qualities rather than substructures in an individual. Qualities that define an individual are related to qualities/parts within other individuals and the whole, the absolute. The whole instantiates itself within each individual via these qualities and relations. Because the whole is realized within each individual the individual contains a piece of the Absolute (or Whole) and thus becomes a person. Persons are related to, and realize the whole, but are not subsumable within it. Thus, individuals are the primary reality in the universe.

This is McTaggart's idea of personhood. He digs into the structure of personhood and defines these persons as special sorts of substances where the term substance is no longer understood as static matter. A substance, as McTaggart understands the term, is that which has qualities and stands in relation to others without itself being a quality or a relation. Every such substance must have content in the form of qualities since persons must have individually determinate character. But how do these qualities impart haecceity or determinate character while also retaining a relation to the Whole? Suppose that a substance is divided into primary parts, A and B. And suppose that each of these parts, again, is divided into parts, AA', AB' and BA', BB', and then each of these is further subdivided into such parts, and so on.

In fact, this is how nature apparently works: division by splitting a parent "cell" into daughter cells and then daughter cells into granddaughter cells is ubiquitous in nature. Note that if this kind of subdivision occurs some of the subparts will possess a one-to-one determining correspondence with the set of primary parent parts—that is they will preserve or precisely repeat some of the content of the primary parts and then the subparts. If these sorts of preservative one-to-one determining correspondence relations arise between parent and daughter parts (either by chance or via some cause), they tend to create repeating patterns in the qualitative makeup of the substance. The subparts and primary parts constitute a repeating pattern and these are what impart the specific identity, or determinate quality to the substance. This kind of subdivision can be continued endlessly with as many permutations as there are qualities, but if a determining correspondence relation arises and repeats itself in the endless subdivisions, then the infinite regress is avoided—at least if what you are interested in concerns which qualities yield the determinate character of the individual/substance. It is those preservative subparts that stand in a determining correspondence relation with the parent/primary parts. We simply take the determining correspondence pattern as the determinate qualitative content of the substance. We do not need to take account of the millions of repeating patterns of the subparts of the substance once we see/identify the crucial determining correspondence pattern. Since the same character is exhibited in the whole and in each of its parts, that character both reflects the Absolute or whole and constitutes the unique personal content of the individual.

I do not wish to argue that McTaggart has succeeded in demonstrating that his "substances"/persons are the primary realities of the universe. My point here is that his argument is philosophically credible and that credible, non-theistic arguments can be and have been advanced by personalist philosophers to establish persons as fundamental. Now personhood can be a key to all of reality whether it is fundamental or derived/emergent. If, for example, you accord persons infinite dignity and ultimate value (as for example Kant did) then persons are ultimate in that ethical sense. Personalism is any philosophy that treats persons as ultimate in some sense. Eschatological personalism as argued in this book treats persons as ultimate both metaphysically and ethically.

In McTaggart's account, a person is an individual whose meaning, content, and uniqueness are derived from his or her set of experienced relations to the entire lived context (i.e. history) or the social-cultural Whole. That relation of the individual to the historical Whole is what constitutes a person because that interaction is where meaning is both received and extracted by the individual. What is the Whole? From an eschatological perspective the whole is what we experience as the "future" eschatological fulfillment or coming of the Kingdom of God. It is in the End of history that the full shape, meaning, and unveiling of the person's life will be revealed. The existentialist philosopher Heidegger presented arguments that seemed to make persons the key to all reality. Interestingly he also linked personhood to the modal experience of the "future". For Heidegger (at least during the time in which he wrote *Being and Time*[6]), the individual's relation to the future, particularly in the form of death, is essential to its constitution. The existence of the individual human being or *Dasein* is a kind of existential stance of rooting or holding itself in the limit or ending, which is its fulfillment. Dasein struggles against concealment and is an unveiling and a shining forth to stand by constructing a world. Dasein is always moving ahead of itself unveiling what is to come. Dasein for Heidegger is modally conditioned by its always moving ahead of itself toward the future and its continual actualization or unveiling of new worlds. Its unveiling of new worlds occurs within a mood of uncanniness and care because the actualization process brings Dasein face to face with its limit in death. For Heidegger death was a kind of fulfillment for Dasein but for an eschatological personalism death is not the final word. We can see how Dasein's activity of unveiling new worlds might be related to Heidegger's account of technology as a kind of distorted form of unveiling. Instead of allowing the things to spontaneously presence, technology sometimes exerts a coercive effect on Dasein.

Heidegger's intuitions concerning the self's rootedness in the future are somewhat unsatisfying. We are not fulfilled in death. Instead, the reason the self is rooted in the future is because the future is essentially a sea of possibilities. We experience possibilities as a kind of freedom. If we collaborate with God, if we align our wills with His, we are free to choose within certain bounds, indicated by the transcendentals beauty, truth, and goodness/love. We actualize those possibilities that realize the infinite manifestations of the good, the true, and the beautiful. The transcendentals structure our very minds, and our very selves into future-oriented teleological agents because we cannot exist, behave, live, or even exercise rationality without aiming for the transcendentals. When we intend anything we aim for what we construe to be the true or the good or the beautiful. Because the transcendentals characterize Being itself, Being is grasped under various aspects of the transcendentals. As such, the transcendentals are the way that we contact and are in-formed by Being or the Real. The transcendentals therefore are inextricably linked to and may be considered a ground for personhood.

The agent intellect

The agent intellect is the name I take from the Aristotelian tradition to denote the creative capacity we each have to bring instances of the transcendentals into existence. It is the capacity to know that we know (insight) and to know/love others and to bring new worlds into existence. It is fundamentally a rational-imaginative capacity. Rational because it can often know when it knows something and when it does not know something. It is sensitive, furthermore, to reasoned dialog in a community of interpreters. It can use and operate under the rules of logic, and empirical evidence. It is imaginative because it can use these tools (logic and sensory evidence, etc.) to vividly simulate and model whatever it desires. It is creative finally because it can call into existence and recognize and appreciate completely novel instances of the transcendentals. The agent intellect has this creative capacity because it is the image of God in us.

Its essence is pure actuality, that is, nothing in it needs to be brought into existence as it is all already actual. This pure actuality makes it possible for it to access control and actualize pure possibilities. This "capacity" can neither be increased, nor diminished. We can intuit what it is like by pointing to the capacity to love, to imagine, to know, to know that I know, to know that I don't know, consent, deny consent, aim-at, intend, build, learn, construct and hope. But all of these things have to be understood as different modes of the more fundamental capacity to love, as love is the essential quality of the agent intellect.

Love underlies all of its knowing, consenting, hoping, constructing, and imagining because love precisely is that capacity to grasp, know, appreciate, reverence, and care for the unique thisness or haecceity of a thing or person. Whenever we cognize some thing in its particularity or uniqueness, we are using the love aspect of the agent intellect to do so. To the extent that we cognize the haecceity of some thing we are loving that thing. Of course, for most things we stop there. We care enough to grasp the thing in its essence and then move on. If we were to continue to cognize and peruse its haecceity we would then begin to care for it and perhaps one day love it. The point is that the cognitive operation of grasping a thing in its essence, the basis of all knowing, is a sub-operation of love. We see this most clearly when we begin to know and ultimately love some other person. We only gradually get to know a person. We learn more and more about that person until over time we feel we really know them. Then love begins to emerge in the relationship. We love that person in virtue of their odd, unique, special, qualities. We love *them*—not some general idea of the person. They become irreplaceable for us because no-one else has that particular combination of qualities. They are unique to that person. Grasping those unique qualities and reverencing them constitute loving that person. The capacity to love another is fully "operational" at all times and its activity can be detected even in cases involving extensive brain damage.

Despite the term "intellect" the operations of the agent intellect should not be construed as aridly intellectual or purely abstractive in nature. In fact, it is more akin to a passion than to an abstractive operation. Love is more of a pouring-out than a perusal. To love is to passionately shower the object of one's love with gifts especially the sacrificial gift of one's Self. To love and to know are intimately connected as you need to know in order to love and to love in order to really, fully know. I cannot fully know an object unless I can grasp both its essence or universal properties and its thingness, haecceity, or uniqueness. To grasp both of these poles (universal and unique) my perusal of the thing in question must encompass engagement with both the essence and the unique qualities of the thing. Only then can I see its relations to other things as well. We need rationality to be passionate in this sense if we are to recover both essence and haecceity in a thing.

Imagination as key to the agent intellect

The passionate nature of the agent intellect is most fully realized in its capacity to form and react to images when it is loving, reasoning or creating. Via its imaginative capacity the agent intellect is ceaselessly bringing potential things (possibles) into existence and this is experienced by us initially as the reception of novel images in our consciousness. Because the agent intellect operates on matter and not the other way around, it is superior to sensible things or matter. Images allow us to operate on matter and transcend sensory information. Matter does not affect the agent intellect as there is nothing in the agent intellect that needs to be actualized or changed. Instead it is the maker and the actuating principle of matter or existents insofar as it brings possibles into existence. It is all actuality; it manifests no potentiality; it never tires from activity. Its intellectual activity never ceases. Its knowledge is actual. This unceasing intellectual activity is felt as a kind of background unity or awareness, a fount of life with intellectual content in consciousness.

Since the agent intellect is superior to things and matter it can imaginatively range over the whole of the individual's life and extract meaning from the past, current, and future. It is an unmixed whole, without parts, and therefore a unity that is indestructible, non-instantiable, and incommunicable with anything else, including other agent intellects. The agent intellect therefore constitutes one of the metaphysical bases of both unity and personhood.

The agent intellect is oriented toward the pick-up and actualization of, what the Aristotelian tradition has called "intelligible forms". Intelligible forms have been understood in several different ways down through the centuries depending on the philosopher's use of the idea. Basically they are forms or the things that allow us to understand both particulars and universals. Some philosophers have understood them as ideas in the Mind of God. Scientifically we might think of them as the resonating strings in string theory or the quantum fields within the quantum flux. But all of these metaphors would be mis-leading unless we conceive of the forms also as *limiting principles*. They demarcate, set-aside, or make sacred a portion of the whole, and that portion can then serve as a "thing" upon which the agent intellect can operate. When calling a form into actuality the agent intellect grasps the form and then adds qualities to it until it becomes a specific thing. It may be that the agent intellect carves out of the flux a portion of the whole and that is called a form. Whether the agent intellect creates these forms or grasps pre-existing forms, once it actually has a form it performs operations on that form. The agent intellect arrives at or creates the haecceity of that form/thing via the ascription to, or addition of qualities to the form. Adding flesh to the bone of a form can be done with almost infinite variety and effort. When love is operative the agent intellect lavishes the intelligible form with special qualities. Think of an author writing a book. That book's unique essence is derived from its endless addition of detail to the story line. Conversely when the agent intellect wants to arrive at universals or knowledge instead of the haecceity of a thing, it grasps the thing's intelligible form and then progressively subtracts qualities until it arrives at the universal or bare form. It can then use that form for creation of knowledge. In short, addition of near infinite detail to a form yields its haecceity or unique identity. This yields knowledge concerning essence and the thing's fundamental relations with other things. The progressive subtraction of qualities from a form, on the other hand, yields knowledge based on universals and causal relations among universals. When the agent intellect operates to subtract qualities from an intelligible form it is operating analytically with the aim to abstraction. On the other hand, if the agent intellect operates to add qualities to an intelligible form it tends toward greater specificity, detail, and sensuousness. The analytic strategy is used most often in focused, directed daytime thinking, while the synthetic strategy is used in more imaginative and "night-time" contexts, such as daydreaming, desire, fantasy, emotional states, and dreams.

Intelligible forms are not only universal or abstract entities. Some intelligible forms should be understood as personifications of divine ideas. These might be thought of as Jung's archetypes or the angels and celestial beings within the Zoroastrian and Abrahamic traditions. These forms can only be encountered passionately when we experience the agent intellect as the "heart" or center of our Being.[7]

What we generally ascribe to the imagination we should ascribe to the agent intellect. Imagination is a speculative mental state with intentional content. It can produce novel ideas or simulate whole worlds without input from the senses. It transcends the senses. It infuses all other faculties of the mind with power. For example, memory or recall would be colorless without the ability to imaginatively re-create scenes from the past. Similarly, desire concerning some future state would be bloodless without imaginatively filling out the contours of that desire. Thinking about other people would be nigh impossible without the ability to imaginatively reconstruct what they are thinking. High-level belief states and propositional attitudes similarly depend on imagination or simulations of the states of affairs that the attitude is about. Even perception, that mental faculty most tied to the senses, is infused with imaginative content, as the predictive processing framework (PPF) makes clear.

The imaginative aspect of the agent intellect is most clearly engaged when we experience what is generally regarded as spiritual content. Science has not adequately charted the spiritual realms delivered to us via the imagi-native powers of the agent intellect. We therefore need to turn to religious studies scholars who have made these imaginal realms their special in-terest. Foremost among these scholars was Henry Corbin. Henry Corbin (1903–1978) studied the mystical texts of the Persian Sufis of the 12th to 13th centuries, especially Suhrawardi (d. 1191) and Ibn Arabi (d. 1240). Corbin claimed[8] that these mystics developed imaginative techniques that gave them access to a realm intermediate between this material world and the immaterial world of God. This intermediate realm he called the mun-dus imaginalis. This is the realm where we material beings can encounter the supernatural realm and God's various names, faces, or manifestations. Corbin identifies the active imagination with the heart or the still point at the center of our Being. We enter the imaginal realm via the heart. We let the images lead us there and we there encounter personifications of a true heart's desire. Images mediate between spirit and matter. They allow spirit to manifest to matter as the image lets them be seen/manifested and they allow matter to see spirit for the same reason. Spirit is given a perceptible form through an image, and matter becomes spiritualized via the image so that its immaterial essence is manifest. For Corbin one of the most crucial encounters in the mundus imaginalis is with one's own angelic intelligence or angel. One's own angel is the divine idea from which one was formed or brought from immateriality into actuality. To encounter it in the imaginal realm is to encounter one's true personality—a tremendously awe-filled ex-perience as it puts one in touch with one's unique destiny, fulfillment, and joy. There is no becoming who you truly are without the encounter with one's own angel.

We have now covered conceptions of the agent intellect that place it as the center of the creative and imaginative nature of personhood, but we have still not exhausted its relevance for understanding the personal. To eluci-date that relevance more clearly we need the modern philosophical tools of "possible worlds" theory.

The agent intellect and possible worlds

This view of the agent intellect as the capacity to imagine other possible worlds, choose some, and bring those worlds into existence is consistent, in my view, with certain versions of David Lewis's Modal Realism, though, of course, Lewis would not endorse any of the theological claims I made above concerning the agent intellect. In Lewis's account[9], the multiverse is composed of an infinity of possible worlds. What are possible worlds? For Lewis possible worlds are of the same ontological kind as our actual world. A world is a maximal, consistent set of spatio-temporally and caus-ally connected stuff. Our world is also a possible world. We say that it is actual simply because we are in it. The only difference between actuality and possibility in this philosophy is that we have an indexical relation to the actual world. A person in a different possible world would say that his world is actual. A possibility obtains or is true if it is true in some possible world. A proposition is necessarily true if it obtains or is true in all possible worlds. In addition to some true propositions obtaining in all possible worlds there must be some things that are objectively right and objectively wrong and these hold in all possible worlds as well. There can never be a world where Auschwitz or intentionally hurting a child is OK.

Instead of one world, there may be an infinity, or at least a plurality of possible worlds. All the ways my life could have gone different are played out in these alternate worlds with each world differing from my actual world sometimes by just minute details. What are the consequences of such an extravagant ontology for personalism? Should we conceive alternate worlds as containing alternate versions of me and you? Is it really me in that alternate world living out exactly the same life course except for one branching event that is different? If there are multiple versions of me across many possible worlds what becomes of my uniqueness? Is my self spread out over worlds just as it is over "time"? Can I really be unique if there are more than one of me or many different versions of me?

For Lewis we cannot have someone in more than one possible world as that would destroy identity. One and the same individual cannot occupy two or more different possible worlds as that would lead to contradiction. If we look at one slice of time how can I be a bachelor in one world and married in another? If we allowed transworld identity where I actually exist in many possible worlds simultaneously then one and the same individual would have different properties in different possible worlds. To avoid such absurdities individuals must be world bound according to Lewis; they cannot move from one world to the next.

Individuals in different possible worlds cannot be identical to one another, but they can bear relations of similarity to one another. If certain individuals in different possible worlds are similar enough in the right respects, then they become *counterparts* of one another. For Lewis, facts about me and what it is possible and impossible for me to do are made true by what my counterparts are doing in different possible worlds.

Given that there are an infinity of possible worlds out there and given that for eschatological personalism a person is a being that uses his agent intellect to call new worlds into Being, i.e. to actualize new worlds, how does that actualization process work? Lewis of course had nothing to say about this so we must speculate here. Actualization must occur phenomenologically as a kind of selection process. There are an indefinite number of worlds vying for actualization and the agent intellect chooses from those worlds that are accessible to it. The selection process is a kind of attentional process where the target worlds are focalized or highlighted and all other accessible worlds are inhibited or pushed away. If the agent intellect chooses on the basis of what best manifests the transcendentals (i.e. choosing in collaboration with God) then the possible world comes to presence and the presencing of that new thing or state of affairs will be in harmony with, and enrich, transform, and transfigure the actual world. Presencing under guidance of the transcendentals is a kind of world exchange where a new world incorporates what was best from the old world but combines it with the new to create a transfigured world. If presencing is guided by the transcendentals the range of possible worlds from which to choose is much wider than when selection is not guided by the transcendentals. When guided by the transcendentals we discover that we can range far beyond what was previously deemed accessible and thus encounter rare and beautiful worlds that we had no idea was available to us. These were "unknown unknowns" to us. In pursuing these actualizations we discover what is genuinely new for our world. Often the actualization process takes on a narrative character as narratives (and poetry) can be construed, in part, as presentations, using the language of chronology and time, of possible worlds coming into being. Narratives testify to the creative abilities of the agent intellect.

If on the other hand, the actualization process is not guided by the transcendentals then what gets actualized is not necessarily in harmony with what is. In fact, most often what gets actualized when not guided by the transcendentals comes from a very restricted range of possible or accessible worlds. These are worlds we keep presencing over and over again as they are the default option when not guided by the transcendentals. Nothing genuinely new is realized. The repeated actualization of non-harmonious but all too familiar states of affairs produces a kind of ontological claustrophobic prison in which mechanical repetition and sameness reign, and there is little to no room for surprises.

Although on Lewis's ontology there is a continuum of many possible worlds—all of which are spatio-temporally and causally isolated from each other, there must be some way that we can have knowledge of these alternate worlds. There must be some way that persons in different worlds can communicate with one another—else how would I know what my counterparts were doing in other worlds? If establishing truth functions depend on my knowledge of counterparts then there must be the possibility of some sort of communication between worlds. If as Lewis claims that each world is just as physically real as ours then there seems to be no a priori reason why worlds cannot interact given that physical objects can interact. There seems to be no in principle reason to insist that worlds cannot interact. I can certainly conceive of possible worlds that are the result of, or best described as products of interactions of other possible worlds. Philosophers have described rules that govern accessibility relations between possible worlds that can be characterized as the extent to which relations between our world and another are reflexive, transitive, or symmetric. For example, our world is morally imperfect. Therefore, its accessibility to a morally perfect world is characterized by transitivity relations but not reflexivity and symmetry. Moral perfection is not accessible in our world and is not reflected in our world but a morally perfect world can be conceived and can affect our world. Ryan[10] has suggested that we can also classify accessibility relations in terms of similarity relations. A world is accessible just in case it is similar in all respects to our world. To the extent that properties of a given world depart from a reference actual world it is less accessible to the reference world. But as argued above we may be able to access worlds that are normally very far from us or inaccessible to us if we are guided by the transcendentals. If, for example, those distant worlds were beautiful, filled with goodness and truth, then the transcendentals would give us access to them, even if they were otherwise dis-similar to us.

But how might inter-world communications take place? It would have to be mediated by the agent intellect as that is the faculty by which we extract intelligibles from things present in our world and it is the faculty by which we access and bring to presence or actualize possible worlds. But communication with other persons in these alternate worlds cannot be exactly like communication between persons in the actual world because each world by definition is different to a greater or lesser degree in terms of their properties, and the more the alternate world departs from the laws, objects, visual characteristics from our reference world, the more we would need to use alternative forms of communication to exchange information with persons in those worlds. I propose that we can communicate or exchange information with alternate worlds via the process of *dreaming*. To see that this is not a completely crazy idea we need to first speak about the many worlds interpretation (MWI) of quantum phenomena.

According to the Everett version of MWI, every time a quantum experiment with different possible outcomes is performed (this arguably obtains for all phenomena exhibiting chaotic dynamics), all outcomes are obtained, but we see only one outcome: the one measured/observed in this world. The other outcomes actually occur but each in a different world. These other unseen worlds are considered absolutely real, just as possible worlds are considered real in Lewis's modal realism. The branching worlds are the ones accessible to us and they obey the laws of physics just as our world does. When the experiment is performed and a measurement occurs the current world is split off, or branches off into a new history. The new world is a duplicate of the parent world up to the last atom but it will have a new history slightly different from and counterfactual to the parent world and beginning from the branching event itself. For a branching event to occur there must be suppression of coherence of the superposition of two localized waveparticle packets (decoherence) with respect to a quantum system's evolving interaction with its internal and external environments. Once decoherence occurs a branching event occurs and a new world is born.

Now to return to our question: can any of these worlds (whether in MWI or in Lewisian framework) interact with one another? Can signals be exchanged between worlds? As mentioned above, Lewis argued that the worlds cannot interact. Nor is it clear if MWI allows interaction between worlds. Some Everettian theorists[11] seem to argue that the alternate worlds are so far away from Earth that information signals cannot be exchanged between the two worlds. If no interaction is possible then individuals are world bound and even though we have counterparts of ourselves in alternate worlds they are not the same as ourselves.

But I suggest that there are some reasons to believe that worlds can interact. As has been pointed out by others, if a counterpart in a Lewisian alternate world has a brain nearly identical to mine as well as similar memories, then he is likely asking whether communication between worlds is possible. I can therefore use my consciousness to infer what my counterpart is thinking. Indeed the more similar the counterpart is to me the more I can infallibly know what the other is thinking (at least at the inception of the branching event) and that is a genuine piece of knowledge about the other world. Another reason to believe that signal exchange between worlds might be possible concerns the issue of freedom. According to the possible worlds framework to say that things could be otherwise for me is to say that there is literally a world where they are in fact different in the relevant way for me. But if no interaction with that other world is possible for me then the fact that the alternative world actually exists in the relevant way is not available to me. If knowledge of the way that things could have been different for me is not available to me then I would not experience counterfactuals in my imagination and dream life, and for all intents and purposes, freedom would be an illusion and I would be living in a world of metaphysical necessity.

But I do experience said counterfactuals and I do experience myself as free and therefore I must have some access to the ideas that things could have been different. Again the only way that things could have gone differently for me in the possible worlds framework is if there are actual worlds where things did in fact go different for my counterpart. I conclude that I have access to that alternate world because I am aware that things could have gone differently for me. I conclude that I am not living in a world of metaphysical necessity and some world exchange or communication with alternate worlds is possible. I can form counterfactuals concerning my experience and do so everyday. It really does seem to be the case that things could have gone differently for me in myriad ways at virtually every instant of my life. Thus, if I accept my experience of free action and contingency in my life as real and if the many worlds idea is correct then some interaction between worlds must be permitted.

Now suppose world boundedness is incorrect or at least can be relaxed as a constraint for both MWI and the possible worlds framework; what follows for prospects of communication between worlds? If communication is possible there is only so much I can do via inference from what I am thinking at present. I may know or infer that my counterpart is thinking about me as his counterpart but how can I see him or exchange signals with him? In addition what about other persons in that alternate world? How can I communicate with them as we do not share brains or minds?

We use our brains to send and receive signals, to communicate with other beings (persons and animals) in this world, so it is likely that some specialized brain system would be required for inter-world communication as well. Those systems within the language faculty and the visual system that deal with alternative possible worlds would likely be important for such communication. But when I engage in counterfactual simulations during some daytime mind-wandering episode do I feel that I am connecting with some alternate world? Perhaps but not really. My reflective, critical mind filters out or inhibits belief commitment to these imaginary worlds during daytime consciousness. It is good of course that we can inhibit belief commitment in these circumstances or we would behave psychotically or at least find it difficult to distinguish reality or the actual from possibility and thus be impaired functionally (to put it mildly).

But note, when I dream about alternative worlds I really do feel and accept and believe that I am in those alternate worlds. It is that ability to accept as true and veridical the possible worlds I am immersed in during the dream state that may allow me to communicate with other "worlds". That acceptance of the "simulations" or hallucinations as real creates psychosis during waking life but opens the possibility for both hallucinatory activity AND possibly, for some occasional, fleeting but real instances of substantive communication with alternate worlds during dream life. Why does merely uncritical acceptance or belief that the simulations index some real world create the possibility for real communication? Because doing so significantly forestalls shutting down the "vision" due to reflective thought, and the signal to noise ratio of the brain/mind system during rapid eye movement (REM) sleep increases. In REM sleep the prefrontal cortex (the brain region that mediates self-critical thought) is down-regulated or relatively inactive while the limbic system and sensory association areas are upregulated. The brain goes into a kind of hyper-receptive mode when the critical faculty is relaxed along with the down-regulation of the dorsal prefrontal cortex. I will say more about this below, but for now, my point is that these two extravagant ideas, i.e. (1) inter-world communication and (2) inter-world communication via the dream state, are not completely without warrant.

Whether or not inter-world communication is possible or even whether or not the Lewisian possible worlds philosophical framework is philosophically viable, its key tenets, I believe, illuminate some aspects of the account of the agent intellect I am developing here. Take for example the issues of freedom and responsibility.

Causation and the agent intellect

The intellect is the primary spiritual organ by which we cognize, strive for, imagine, and grasp the transcendentals. That striving is an agentic force. We have seen that Aristotelian tradition called this form of the intellect, the *agent intellect*. The agent intellect (God's or other persons) is the only thing in the universe that can bring possible worlds into Being. This great creative capacity is a defining feature of human persons. The activity of the agent intellect is not the same thing as what philosophers call "agent causation". Agent causation is distinguished from event causation (assuming that event causation even exists) in that agents have the power to cause effects as well as the power to not cause effects. That power furthermore is exercised freely—at will. Finally, it is future-oriented and purposive in that it contains intellectual content in the form of intentional states associated with reasons, desires, and beliefs. Event causation has none of these features.

The agent intellect on the other hand does not really involve agent causation. Bringing worlds into existence is not strictly a causal process. Bringing things into existence is really just allowing some things to *presence* while ignoring other things. To that extent the agent intellect (like agent causation) manifests free choice and intentional states. Allowing some things to presence simultaneously dis-allows or inhibits other worlds from presencing. This selection process both looks like free choice/activity and is free activity. Within a philosophical framework roughly like that of Lewis's modal realism, reality is a plenitude. It contains all possible worlds. Given some sort of theoretical framework like Lewisian possible worlds, it is reasonable to suppose that when the agent intellect brings one of these worlds into existence, it simply selects the target world and basically acknowledges it, or allows it to presence, while ignoring or inhibiting presencing of the rest. Its selection of one world over all others can involve use of sensory information to develop future-oriented intentional states and mental models that facilitate the presencing process. This involves extraction of information or what the Aristotelian tradition called intelligible forms from objects in the world. Our intentional states construct models of extramental realities by stripping them of their accidental or inessential qualities and abstracting operational or essential characteristics (intelligible forms) until the mind has a highly accurate image, mental model, or predictive simulation of the target object or reality. In other words, and consistent with the PPF assumed in this book, the mind knows reality via a concept that is analogous to, or a simulation of an object or reality. This is the nature of the agent intellect's abstractive intuition of Being. It calls possible worlds into Being and it extracts intelligible forms from things already in existence.

Both possibilities and intelligible forms can also be construed as essences. An essence is that which a thing is. When it is not lodged in an existent, it can be thought of as an idea in the Mind of God or a possible thing or world relative to some existent world. When it is moved by an agent intellect out of the realm of the possible and into the realm of the actual it becomes an individual nature or thing. But what makes one individual nature or thing unique is that which exercises existence or action in the thing (the "suppositum/subsistence"). For human beings that is the agent intellect. The agent intellect exercises the received act of existence by creatively presencing intelligible forms and/or other possible worlds. Essence is that by which something exists as what it is, existence is that which actualizes an essence, and subsistence is that which is able to accomplish the "actualizing". The actualizing capacity (agent intellect), furthermore, ensures that the existence or nature that comes into Being in the actualization process is its own, unique, and incommunicable nature.

But how does the agent intellect perform this almost magical feat of bringing something from out of the realm of the possible and into the realm of the actual? One clue is that when an intentional state is focused on an already existent thing, the actualization process involves abstraction, that is, the inhibition of inessential properties and the extraction of the essential properties (essence or intelligible form) of a thing. Those essential properties can be construed as what the thing was before it came into existence, i.e. its form when in the realm of the possible. So, when the agent intellect seeks to actualize a non-existent possible thing, it performs the opposite operation: instead of subtracting/abstracting accidental properties from the form/idea/possibility, it allows a form to presence, and then it adds qualities/properties to it, and this is what we know as existence. Eliminate accidental qualities you have the intelligible form or raw possible—the elements that make up a mental simulation. Add accidental qualities to the intelligible form and you get individualized existent things.

But the agent intellect is not only a process that grasps worlds and intelligible forms. It also "knows" them in their haecceity or uniqueness. It has to "know" them as unique entities—otherwise it could not extract or add accidentals. To know something in its essence or uniqueness is a form of loving that thing.

Love as the eschatological operation of the agent intellect

Theologically, a person is a being called into existence by God, loved by God, and then given an invitation by God to collaborate with God in stewardship of creation and creativity. God's love confers on the individual that individual's qualitative content and uniqueness. Love cannot be love unless it concerns the "who" or the subjectivity of the beloved. It seeks the best for THIS individual because of his/her thisness/haecceity. Each one of us responds differently to the invitation given to us by the Absolute or by God and this response helps to constitute our personhood, our ethical personhood. Love requires the self-donation of each person to the other, which, in turn, requires that each person to have a self to give away. To have a self to give away one must love oneself or hold in reverence one's dignity and uniqueness. Thus, love constitutes personhood for the lover. In addition, love constitutes personhood for the beloved. Insofar as love concerns the unique qualities and radiance associated with the unrepeatable individual who is the beloved, then love also helps to constitute the beloved. Thus, love constitutes personhood for both lover and the beloved.

The eschatological moods and modes are the three theological virtues of faith, hope, and love. Because social relations and transcendence to these relations (via the eschatological virtues) help to define the human person, he or she is necessarily an ethical being. For personalists it is not just any social relations that best facilitate emergence of personhood. Indeed, some social relations can actively inhibit personhood (I will discuss these in a later chapter). For the personalists I build upon in this book the phenomenon of love is the social relation that best promotes transcendence and best elicits the unique ethical content of the human person. Love needs to be understood at all levels, biologically, psychologically, culturally, and theologically, if one is to understand personhood. Love necessarily picks out the uniqueness of each individual, as well as ignites hope and faith in that individual and thus elicits personhood in that individual. Person depends crucially on the social relation Love.

Psychologically a child becomes a unique person by being loved by others. If the world fails to love the child, personalist theologians would say that God still loves that child and that love individuates that child; it allows for transcendence beyond the web of social relations that envelop the child. Parents' love for the child is selective and encompasses all of the child's self, quirks, and all. The child is made unique by love so that the child cannot be a mere reflection of the social relations he finds himself within. In adulthood love still operates to individuate the human being. Sexual love is once again selective and encompasses the unique qualities of the beloved. Love is also meaning-dependent in the sense that the surrounding culture both facilitates and inhibits its expressions. The culture, by providing the symbols that potentiate the allowable modes of expression for personal love, shapes and canalizes expressions of personal love. Some cultures promote a wider range of expressions of love than others.

In short, for most personalists love is the social relation that individuates a human being and constitutes his personhood. The basic datum of reality is Love, because God is Love. Love is not a substance but an activity. God is actus purus (pure act) but that pure act is freedom and Love. Love implies personality and therefore personality or personhood is the fundamental reality of the universe.

Love is another name for the activity of the agent intellect but then how can the agent intellect go wrong? We are certainly not always loving creatures.

Agency, free will, and sin

In the Prologue to the Second Part of the Summa, St Thomas Aquinas follows St Damascene's notion of what it means for persons to be made in the image and likeness of God: "[M]an is said to be made to God's image, in so far as the image implies *an intelligent being endowed with free-will and self-movement*[12]" (Aquinas ST Prologue, Second Part, emphases mine). In short, inasmuch as man operates as an autarch, utilizes his intelligence to inform his free creative activity, and is the principle and controller of his own actions, it can be said that man is made in the image and likeness of God. *A person therefore is a being who can use his free intelligent creative activity as embodied by the agent intellect to know and love other persons, and bring new things and worlds into being from out of the realm of possibility.* When a man forfeits his calling to act as a free agent, to use his intelligence to choose wisely then he also to some extent forfeits his personality and integrity. Or if, more commonly, a group intervenes and functionally takes over control of the man's actions, then that group obscures the image of God within that man and his integrity is impaired. Man's will is free only when it is informed by rationality and is aligned with the transcendentals and the truth about the world and the values contained therein. Irrational deliberations corrupt the will and thereby compromise autarchy or self-control of actions. Conversely, the will can corrupt rational deliberations if the will is not rooted in and guided by Love. In addition, if we privilege either the will or rational deliberation when it comes to choosing, free choice once again becomes compromised as choice cannot rely on mere will or mere deliberation but on the proper relationship and balanced interaction between the two.

How then do we properly balance will and deliberation? We do so by engaging the logos or rationality or the intentional states of the individual. Metaphysically this means engaging in some kind of collaboration with God or logos. Intentional states translate directives of the rational deliberative process into the beliefs, desires, and drives of the will so that the will can direct implementation of an action. Formation of intentional states is dependent on the deliberative process, which, in turn, is dependent on prudence, wisdom, and conscience, i.e. collaboration with God. But if we choose to refuse the collaboration with God we become divided selves and then the agent-intellect's operations can falter. Deliberation and will can err due to a corrupted intentional state resulting from a poorly formed conscience. A false conscience at the level of the intellect can be due to "invincible ignorance", in which the individual, through no fault of his own, has not obtained formation of a true conscience. False conscience also can be due to culpable or willful ignorance when the individual simply resists what he knows to be the true and good choice of action. This seems to be what St Augustine did when he stole those pears as a youth. He simply ignored what he knew was right and good and acted perversely to please his comrades.

St Thomas argues, however, that Augustine did not choose that course of action simply out of a perverse inclination to mock the good. He was, after all, stealing pears, to please a group of his friends. This insight alerts us to a great source of evil in this transitional age we are passing through—the group, or crowd, that pressures and dissolves individual conscience. In the modern age crowds are invariably influenced by or controlled by states and machines. When Augustine stole those pears as a child he was seeking adulation and approval from his comrades, his local pressure group at the time. It was not sheer perversity. He forfeited his own conscience for the gang mentality. The group's intentional state ("be transgressive") replaced his individual intentional state ("please your friends"). All actions, according to Aquinas, aim at some good (the first principle of practical reason). But to avoid missing that mark you need the guidance of conscience rooted in the agent intellect. Synderesis refers to an operation of the agent intellect we call the conscience (a linking up with God as law and logos) that helps us to aim at the true, the good, and the beautiful, and to avoid missing the mark. Synderesis therefore must depend on the intentionality inherent in the agent intellect. We use intentional states to aim at the true, the good, and the beautiful. We access these states via synderesis. Synderesis is a resonance or linking up of the individual agent's aims with the transcendentals such that the individual brings into Being, with his choices and actions, instances of the true, the good, and the beautiful.

Aquinas tells us that reason (and by inference intentional states) is the essential aspect of the human person/agent in that it functions to support activation or unveiling of synderesis. Reason as synderesis makes possible the rational pursuit of worthy goals, of the true, the good, and the beautiful. Intentional states also are fundamental to cognition itself and therefore both inform and are informed by the deliberative process. We use intentional states to grasp intelligible species of the "forms" or those things/concepts that inform the nature of the thing in question and that are made real or actualized in awareness by the cognitional process. Forms exist in some ontological realm of Platonic possibilities or eternal objects. Or perhaps they are ideas in the Mind of God. Or perhaps possibilities are created whenever a mind or agent intellect is created. When God offers existence to an individual and the individual accepts the gift, the gift includes a near infinite realm of possibilities associated with the individual's mind, and the individual's task is to daily choose which of those possibilities he will attempt to actualize. That is the basis of free will. Unactualized possibilities are forms that are compossible with the individual's world (potentials) or impossible with respect to the individual's world. Intelligible forms that are currently actual can also be taken up by the agent intellect and made into new existents and this too is part of the free activity of the individual.

In his analysis of the problem of free will,[13] Aquinas points out that the intelligible forms taken in by the mind are "...general forms covering a number of individual things, so that the willed tendencies (of an individual) remain open to more than one course of action..." The agent intellect prefers to grasp intelligible forms in existent things and turn them into universals so that new knowledge can be created. The mind processes "forms"—that are like general categories or universals that capture a range of more primitive natural kinds...and that generality, that ability to abstract away from specific instances and to entertain a range of specific (counterfactual) outcomes, confers on human beings an additional type of freedom from compulsion to enact any one specific aim or outcome. "The architect's concept of the house, for example, is general enough to cover many different house plans, so that his will can tend towards making the house square, round or some other shape".[14]

Aquinas's concept concerning the power of the agent intellect is consistent in certain respects with eschatological personalism's concept of the agent intellect. For Aquinas, the agent intellect, via its grasp of intelligible forms, gives us the ability to form general concepts that abstract away from specific stimuli and capture large amounts of information, thus allowing us to entertain many different ways to attain a goal. We are, as it were, given a range of choices to accomplish the same goal. That range of choices confers on us: (1) enhanced chances at success in achieving that goal (if one means does not work we can try another); (2) freedom from a pull toward or slavery to the most salient stimuli in any given context (often the most salient are not the most wise choices); (3) a growing awareness of the responsibility to engage in a thoroughgoing deliberative process about choices as poor choices hurt more than just the chooser; and (4) an enhanced pressure to develop reliable procedures for ranking choices along some value hierarchy, i.e. a valid criteria for choosing.

The agent intellect however does much more than just form general concepts from the forms *in potentia*. In his commentary on Aristotle's *De Anima*[15] in the chapter on the agent intellect, Aquinas notes that Aristotle's treatment of agency moves away from the selection of the Platonic ideas as the basic constituents of mind. Instead Aristotle proposes a general power of the agent intellect to bring into actuality forms that had only potential existence until the active intellect grasped them and pulled them into being. The abstractive process not only reveals the universals subsisting in forms but also transforms these forms into new concepts that can link up with other images in consciousness (the so-called phantasms) so that this complex set of concepts/images can cumulate knowledge and guide choice and action in the real world. The power to make actual what was previously only potentially true, good, and beautiful is the essence of Mind for Aquinas and it is the essence of personhood for us.

But, for Aquinas, potential existence cannot be a form of Being as Being is actual or existent. Nevertheless, potential existence is not mere nothingness. It seems reasonable to postulate a realm of potential forms related to the Mind of God as well as a second realm of potentials not created by God but the products of the free activity of all of his created creatures, men, angels, dominions, hierarchies, etc. We have called this intermediate realm a liminal realm. A non-theist, of course, can also entertain an intermediate realm between Being and non-being. Whatever the metaphysical status of the realm of potential forms there is no doubt that Augustine and Aquinas believed it impacted Being and that it along with God's creative activity was a source of Being. When in communion with God that intermediate realm for us is the possibilities in the Mind of God. When not in communion with

God that intermediate realm is something created by us and other fallen creatures. It is a measure of the importance of the agent intellect that all philosophers in the Aristotelian tradition ascribed to it the ability to access these intermediate realms for better or ill. The fundamental function of the agent intellect is to access the realm of possibilities associated with God and bring these possibilities into Being. But that fundamental function is distorted when communion with God is lost. We can still bring worlds into Being but the possibilities we select from are no longer or less often from the Mind of God.

In addition to the abstractive activity of the agent intellect, the agent intellect has the ability to separate the mind from the immediate stimulus environment and from matter more generally. The agent intellect or the individual who realizes his active powers is not acted upon and instead acts. The agent intellect allows the person to develop a relative autonomy with respect to the immediate environment. It allows the individual to delay gratification of impulses in favor of some future better gratification. This capacity to delay gratification for some future good is fundamental to autarchy. Thus, the idea of freedom from the immediate stimulus and the idea of the future, two ideas fundamental to autarchy, are linked to the activity of the agent intellect. That freedom from immediate stimulus and context does not mean that the individual is separate from the environment or the social and historical context. It merely means that his actions cannot be reduced to that context or to the immediate "now". He or she has some elbow or breathing room. He is not obliged to respond to every stimulus that crosses his path no matter how salient. Instead, he acts upon those stimuli that he chooses to act upon. And he abstracts from those stimuli various and manifold "concepts" that then become the raw material (in memory or the passive intellect) for further building up of his autonomy, abstractive powers, and freedom. Let us call this high conception of the agent the "autarchic agent" or autarch.

Aquinas points out that while free will comes from the deliberation around alternative courses of action, the exercise of the free will itself "... comes from an agent causing the action in pursuance of a goal, so that the first source of an activity's exercise is some goal[16]" (p. 177). Goal-directed behaviors set or intended by autarchic agents are the normal arena in which free will operates.

> And if we take note of the objects of mind and of will we will find that the mind's object is what holds first place in the world of form-namely being and truth-whilst will's object is what holds first place in the world of goals-namely, good; and that good applies to all goals just as truth applies to all forms mind takes in, so that good itself as taken in by the mind is one truth among others, and truth itself as goal of mind's activity is one good among others.[17]

The highest good and purpose of Mind and will is to seek the good and know the truth. The stuff of the good and the true is love—that much sullied but still necessary word. Love is the super-ordinate and ultimate goals of all other goals. It, in turn, sets the standard for a hierarchy of values and a criterion upon which goals can be evaluated. The closer the goal is to the good and the true and the beautiful, the better the goal. When Love guides the deliberative or intentional process, free will can intend the true, the beautiful, and the good, and attain to it. When Love guides the operations of the agent intellect the agent intellect fully realizes the being of the forms it grasps and fully brings those forms to fullness of Being because those forms are ultimately intended by God.

When something besides Love or the transcendentals guide the operations of the agent intellect in interaction with the Will, the forms gasped by the agent intellect are either not fully realized or are missed entirely and other forms are realized. Sometimes these other forms are things that should not exist and should not be brought into being because they contradict natural law or God's will. Before stealing pears becomes the crime that it is, it is an idea or image that has to be abstracted from forms *in potentia*. In this case the forms *in potentia* come out of the liminal realm of possibles created by human and other persons (?fallen angels, angels, etc.) rather than the Mind of God. According to Aquinas this is where all ideas come from—from apprehension of forms *in potentia*. But there are two such realms: (1) the possibles that exist as ideas in the Mind of God and (2) the possibles associated with the liminal realm associated with minds of creatures. Christ said evil comes out of the heart of man and the heart is where thoughts and images dwell. "For out of the heart proceed evil thoughts, murders, adulteries, fornications, thefts, false witness, blasphemies...[18]" Since some acts derived from these images are objectively evil, there must be forms that are also objectively evil or things that should not be brought into existence. When these criminal ideas are brought from the realm of the possible into being, into the Mind of an actor and inserted into the intentional states of an actor they are in danger of being enacted.

Both images and acts can be good or evil. Some images and acts are evil under all circumstances. Good intentions cannot make an objectively evil image or act good. The objective nature of the image or act itself, whether it is good or bad, is determined by the relation of man's freedom with the good, with God, who alone is good.[19] As the personalist John Paul II noted:

> The morality of acts is defined by the relationship of man's freedom with the authentic good...Acting is morally good when the choices of freedom are in conformity with man's true good and thus expresses the voluntary ordering of the person towards his ultimate end: God himself, the supreme good in whom man finds his full and perfect happiness.[20]
>
> (VS 91)

The good is something not made by us but discovered by us through creative activity of realizing a possibility via reason and revelation. It is therefore outside of us and is experienced as an objective fact encountered by us. It is not something we invent and then infuse into the act. We "realize" it. Our intentions therefore cannot make an evil image or act good, because the act and the image have an objective and ontological status independent of the intention. When we order our intentions to the true, the good, and the beautiful our intentions are moral. How do we order our intentions rightly and how do our intentions become corrupt and a source of evil? Aquinas says that we need synderesis and prudence to order our intentions rightly and that this dependence on prudence also opens the door to evil.

When an individual deliberates around some potential action, he entertains a welter of images brought up from non-being or the realm of the possibles by the agent intellect. To deliberate wisely over these images prudence provides counsel and judgment. Counsel (eubulia) prompts the individual to obtain information relevant to the case from outside trustworthy sources. Judgment weighs the options for courses of action and issues a judgment on the preferred action.

It is through counsel obtained from experience and from trusted others that prudence draws upon moral and cultural norms to make an informed judgment about what course of action to pursue. We necessarily seek out counsel from others when formulating intentions and thus we become vulnerable to counsel received from local groups. It is here that evil enters the picture. If prudence is corrupted by evil counsel then intentions become distorted as well.

When operating optimally under a well-informed prudential wisdom, the will allows itself to be informed by rational deliberation and then to choose the true, the good, and the beautiful. The cognitional process of apprehending universals from potential forms also operates optimally and the true, the good, and the beautiful are brought into being by the agent intellect. When prudential counsel is corrupted, however, via connection with corrupted counsels or groups, the will receives corrupted counsel from the rational, deliberative process, and therefore its cognitional operations are biased, disordered, or only partially implemented. St Thomas says that evil derives from a "...certain good joined to the privation of another good; as the end proposed by the intemperate man[21]". The privation of evil is linked to the ends or intentional states of an intemperate or disordered man. Aquinas places the source of evil squarely in the lap of the agent.

> ...In the action, evil is caused by reason of the defect of some principle of action, either of the principal or the instrumental agent; thus the defect in the movement of an animal may happen by reason of the weakness of the motive power, as in the case of children, or by reason only of the ineptitude of the instrument, as in the lame. On the other hand, evil is caused in a thing, but not in the proper effect of the agent, sometimes

by the power of the agent, sometimes by reason of a defect, either of the agent or of the matter. It is caused by reason of the power or perfection of the agent when there necessarily follows on the form intended by the agent the privation of another form; as, for instance, when on the form of fire there follows the privation of the form of air or of water.[22]

Aquinas points out that the agent intellect can break down in two ways: it can operate weakly as in the case of the lame man or the child, or it can go into hyperdrive so to speak "by reason of the power or perfection of the agent when there necessarily follows on the form intended by the agent the privation of another form". Here Aquinas points to the "form intended by the agent" as the key to identification of the privation of another form that is the source of evil. When a faulty or corrupted intentional state grasps a potential form when some other form representing a genuine good was intended by the agent, there is privation linked to that other form not intended by the agent as that targeted intention was faulty. For example, when an individual accepts a false, pale imitation of a thing when aiming for the true instance of that thing, then he misses his mark and brings the pale imitation into existence. When an individual turns away from collaboration with God, his intentional states are then informed by local cultural norms or powerful groups rather than by the transcendentals. If he aims in his creative activity for realization of an idea that would increase his power or the power of the local group, he is aiming for realization of a good. The good in this case is Power. But that aim and good is missing the regulative ideal of the transcendentals. Power without truth or prudence tends to evil and chaos. So the good that is realized is a kind of power that does not manifest the true, the good, and the beautiful. Instead it becomes naked force and is then mobilized by the group for nefarious ends. So evil is a privation but it is also associated with bringing into being some "thing" that has a kind of twilight existence in the liminal realm subject to entropy and decay. Thus, eschatological personalism suggests a new conception of evil.

The agent intellect is central to the personalist project and the human drama more generally as it is the seat of freedom in our lives and therefore linked to good and evil in our lives. It constitutes the core of creative activity of the person and it is the power that brings possibilities into Being. When we refuse the collaboration with God we become vulnerable to local group and cultural influences and we use these criteria instead of the transcendental to decide which worlds or things to bring into Being. Without guidance from the transcendentals the things we actualize are all too often destructive, monstrous, or subject to futility. We experience this kind of futile activity as fallenness. It is a form of subjectivity that is limited by Time or temporality. All things decay. All things pass away or are subject to the law of entropy within this liminal realm which is what we have when we refuse the collaboration with God. But the incarnation inaugurates another kind of temporality that is defined by eschatological hope.

Notes

1 Bayne, T. & D.J. Chalmers, "What is the unity of consciousness?", in Cleeremans 2003: pp. 23–25. Cleeremans, Axel (ed.), 2003, *The unity of consciousness: Binding, integration and dissociation*. Oxford: Oxford University Press.
2 Moll, J., et al. "The self as a moral agent: Linking the neural bases of social agency and moral sensitivity." *Social Neuroscience* 2.3–4 (2007): 336–352.
3 Crosby, J.F. *The selfhood of the human person*. Washington, DC: The Catholic University of America Press, 1996. Crosby is a prolific personalist author who has written in-depth assessments of personalist themes in several Catholic convert figures, such as the philosophers Max Scheler (who converted briefly to the Catholic Church), Edith Stein (who converted from Judaism to Catholicism and entered the Carmelite order before she was murdered by the Nazis), Dietrich von Hildebrand, and the convert from Anglicanism Cardinal John Henry Newman. There are other Catholic philosophers who have written profound works on personality. Robert Spaemann (Spaemann, R. *Persons: The difference between 'someone' and 'something'*. Oxford: Oxford University Press, 1996/2012) stressed that person was a higher level of Being beyond particularity or universality. Persons can comprehend universal natures in thought and therefore are situated beyond universality. Personality for Spaemann is more like a paradigm of Being and when thought thinks Being itself it transcends its intentional content, i.e. it transcends itself. Persons are this relational excess always transcending themselves in freedom. For Robert Sokolowski (Sokolowski, R. *Phenomenology of the human person*. Cambridge: Cambridge University Press, 2008) persons are the kinds of things to which being is exposed in truth. We experience that unveiling of Being when we know that we know. But if persons are knowers of truth then Sokolowski returns again and again (as do I in this book) to the problem of the intelligibility of things as forms. He roots our ability to ascertain the truth in reason, of course, but interestingly roots reason in language and syntax rather than semantics as well as the act of predication or what I would call adding qualities to an intelligible form. I see reason as more firmly linked to imagination than to language and syntax unless syntax itself can be modeled as imaginative cognition.
4 Gracia, J.J.E. *Individuality: An essay on the foundations of metaphysics*. Albany: State University of New York Press, 1988.
5 McTaggart, J.T.E. *The nature of existence*. Vol. 1. Cambridge: Cambridge University Press, 1921; Vol. 2; C.D. Broad (Ed.), Cambridge University Press, 1927.
6 Heidegger, M. *Being and time*, translated by J. Macquarrie and E. Robinson. Oxford: Basil Blackwell, 1962 (first published in 1927). Reacting to Heidegger, the French philosopher Jean-Paul Sartre also seemed to conceive persons as at least in part to be future-oriented as they were constituted by the life project they chose to dedicate themselves to. For Sartre an individual is free but that freedom is experienced not as open future and possibility, but as terror and nihilation. Persons, Sartre said, are condemned to be free until they build a life project. A person is defined by the life-project he chooses to realize or become.
7 The Aristotelian tradition often contrasted the agent or active intellect with the passive intellect. The passive intellect received sensible forms and then passed these along to the agent intellect. In this work, I assign both the intentional and the receptive capacities to the agent intellect, treating each as one pole within an active-passive, dipolar phenomenon.
8 Corbin, H. (1969). *Creative imagination in the Sufism of Ibn 'Arabi*, translated by R. Manheim. Original French, 1958. Princeton, NJ: Princeton University Press. For an excellent overview of Corbin's work on the imagination as a

spiritual faculty see Cheetham, T. *All the world an icon: Henry Corbin and the angelic function of beings.* Berkeley, CA: North Atlantic Books, 2012.

9 Lewis, D. *On the plurality of worlds.* Oxford: Blackwell Publishers, 1986.

10 Ryan, M.L. *Possible worlds, artificial intelligence and narrative theory.* Bloomington: Indiana University Press, 1991.

11 See Kaku, M. *Parallel universes: A journey through creation, higher dimensions and the future of the cosmos.* New York: Random Doubleday, 2005, for a popular account of the scientific debates around the many worlds interpretation of quantum effects.

12 "Since, as Damascene states (De Fide Orth. ii, 12), man is said to be made in God's image, in so far as the image implies "an intelligent being endowed with free-will and self-movement...": Summa Theolgiae, Prologue First Part of Second Part.

13 Aquinas, T. "*Aquinas, selected philosophical writings*, translated and edited by T. McDermott." Oxford: B. Blackwell, 1993. pp. 176–183.

14 Aquinas, p. 176.

15 Aquinas, T. *Aristotle's De Anima: In the version of William of Moerbeke and the commentary of St. Thomas Aquinas.* Eugene, OR: Wipf and Stock Publishers, 2007.

16 Aquinas, p. 177.

17 Aquinas (p. 177).

18 Bible-Matthew. *The Gospel of St. Matthew.* (1984) 15:19.

19 VS 91.

20 Pope John Paul II. Veritatis Splendor (VS) *The splendor of truth.* Boston, MA: Pauline Books & Media, 1993. Print.

21 Aquinas, ST I 48, 5.

22 Aquinas ST I 48, 5.

4 The eschatological dream time

Eschatological personalism entails a different sense of time, a different temporal experience than the standard experience, and this fact carries interesting consequences for the shape and feel of personality for the eschatological personalist. In fact, the eschatological personalist freely navigates between two different temporalities and timelines: one characterized by necessity and futility and the other characterized by freedom and hope. There is the current age and there is the already-begun, but not-yet fully arrived coming age of the Kingdom of God. The sense of living as a pilgrim in the current age on the way to the blessed Kingdom of the coming age comes right out of the entire eschatological tradition from Zoroaster right up to the early Christian New Testament texts and the visionary texts of Second Temple period Jewish apocalyptic literature. The visionary, dream-like nature of these texts makes them powerfully inspirational but dangerous when mis-interpreted. These texts when interpreted as justification for utopian and revolutionary violence have been soaked in blood down through the centuries so utmost care must be taken to interpret them responsibly. To do so correctly the eschatological personalist once again invokes the transcendentals. If an interpretation leads to or involves loving realization of the inherent worth and dignity of each and every individual as well as new manifestations of the true, the good, and the beautiful, then the visions and dreams and images may be from God—otherwise they are likely to lead to destructiveness of one kind or another. That does not mean that the eschatological personalist is some kind of non-violent, milquetoast pacifist. War and killing "infinitely valuable persons" are sometimes justified. "Just war theory" addresses those times when killing is justified. The point here is that many wars and many acts of violence cannot be justified, particularly with apocalyptic texts and we should err on the side of non-violent responses at all times.

More than any other scriptural text, the *Book of Revelation* has informed eschatological thought and the experience of temporality in the Christian tradition. The book is divided into a visionary prologue (1:1–8), an epistolary introduction (1:9–3:22), cycles of visions (4:1–22:9), and an epilogue and epistolary conclusion (22:10–21). Its visionary character, its horrific imagery concerning the consequences of sin, and its evocation of two ages (the age of wrath and the coming age of fulfillment) that the believer must navigate all make the book an essential text for eschatological Christianity. A believer simultaneously participates in both the age of wrath and the blessed age, but with progressively increased anchoring of the self in the blessed age. That anchoring, that shifting of the identity from the current to the blessed age is slowly accomplished over time with the help of traditional Christian ascetical, ritual, sacramental, and ecclesial practices. As the eschatological orientation begins to predominate in the consciousness of the believer, he can say along with St Paul, that "...it is no longer I that lives, but Christ liveth in me" (Galatians 2: 20). Jesus Christ is the true revelation of the *personal* and personality. The believer's true identity is slowly unveiled and realized as Christ-like. and the person's destiny is revealed as the already accomplished fulfillment of God's redemptive promises in the blessed age. Entry into the blessed age is accomplished through participation in the Christian community, "being washed in the blood of the Lamb", being "sealed", and rising above the corruption of the current age via self-rule or "conquering" as the Lamb of God conquered.

The two ages overlap and there is a gate between them. Passage through the gate is closed except for those who have "washed one's robes in the blood of the Lamb". The eschatological personalist seeks to become one of the elect or the "sealed" in order to pass between the two ages while being anchored in the blessed age. While the believer must live out his or her appointed time in this age, to the extent his identity is anchored in the blessed age, his or her true Self is not shaped by any force in the current age. Instead his identity is confirmed with a seal placed on the soul while his name is written in the *Book of Life* (Rev 20:12). The age of wrath is passing away as the new age, the new creation, the new Heaven, and the new Earth are more and more fully realized. All Christians, living and dead, stand as one community before the Throne of God from the perspective of the new creation.

The age of wrath is the age of decision. Every person must make a decision for or against the Lamb of God. Neutrality is no longer possible. The son of Man vomits out the lukewarm. The decision is either to collaborate with God or not to do so. Attempting to bring possible worlds into being without God leads too often to horrors. The person who tries to birth new worlds without God typically births horrors instead of the utopias intended. To aim for utopia without God is literally to miss the target, to sin. On the other hand, those persons who decide for God, if they are steadfast in that decision and if they persevere, naturally bring into Being the new Heaven and new Earth; they bring into Being the Kingdom of God. They can do so because they are taken out of this age and placed before the Throne of God in the new age, where they become the elect. They can then navigate through the age of wrath without succumbing to slavery or folly. The decision to follow the Lamb and to "conquer as he conquered" results in a seal or mark that makes the believer capable of traversing the two ages in order to collaborate with God.

Dreams and visions are crucial for eschatological personalism and they appear to facilitate entry into the coming age via the "sealing". The Revelation of Jesus Christ is communicated to John of Patmos through prophetic visions (1:1–9). John is instructed by "one like a Son of Man", a title Jesus ascribed to himself, to communicate a series of images and warnings to the seven churches of Asia (1:10–13). The "one like a son of man" reveals what the seven stars and seven lampstands represent (1:14–20). Mostly the messages are to hold steadfast to the true faith despite trials and tribulations of this world. Various powers and gifts are promised to those who remain faithful to the name of Jesus. For example, those who overcome will be given the hidden manna to eat and a white stone with a secret name on it (2:12–17). They will be clothed in white garments, and their names will not be blotted out from the *Book of Life*; their names will also be confessed before the Father and His angels (3:1–6), and they will be granted the opportunity to sit with the Son of God on His throne (3:14–22). Since that throne implies power to rule and power to create, the faithful will do both in the age to come (which paradoxically is already begun).

At the Throne of God there are 24 elders seated on thrones (4:1–5) and four living creatures stand ready (4:6–11). A scroll, with seven seals, is presented, and it is declared that the Lion of the tribe of Judah will open this scroll in the future (5:1–5). The "Lamb having seven horns and seven eyes" takes the scroll, and the seven seals are opened one by one. With the opening of the first seal four horsemen are unleashed. The leading horse is white, the second horse is red, the third is black, and the last is a pale horse whose rider is Death. The horsemen carry weapons to scourge the earth and its sinners.

At the opening of the fifth seal, we see martyrs and believers being given white robes and protected, while the sixth seal opening unleashes earthquakes that blacken the skies, sun, and moon. The stars of heaven fall to the earth. 144,000 persons from the 12 Tribes of Israel are sealed as servants of God on their foreheads (7:1–8). They stand before the Throne of God, clothed with robes made "white in the blood of the Lamb" and then the seventh seal is opened, announcing seven trumpets to be sounded by seven angels, and along with them further calamities for the current age of wrath. But there is calm before the storm when the seventh seal is opened: "Silence in heaven for about half an hour" (8:1). Then the first trumpet is sounded. Hail and fire, mingled with blood, are thrown to the earth. The Second Trumpet causes a burning mountain to fall from the sky destroying the oceans. With the third trumpet a great star, named Wormwood, falls from heaven and poisons the earth's waters (8:10–11) The Fourth Trumpet causes a darkening of the sun, moon, and stars. The fifth trumpet opens up a bottomless pit which spews forth smoke (9:2). From out of the smoke, human-locust hybrids emerge with breastplates of iron (like machines) who emit deafening sounds and who plague anyone who was not given the "seal of God" on their foreheads (9:4). With the sixth trumpet armies kill a third of mankind by plagues of fire, smoke, and brimstone.

Then another angel appears crying out mysteries that are like thunders and that are not to be written down by John. John has to eat the scroll to prophesy. With the seventh trumpet seven golden bowls and seven superhuman figures appear (11:15–19). A Woman "clothed with the Sun" appears. The Church has often interpreted this figure to be Mary Mother of Jesus. She wears a crown of heaven and stands athwart the moon. She is about to give birth to a male child (12:1–2). A Dragon waits for the birth of the child so he can devour it. But the child is protected by the Throne of God, and the woman hides in a place prepared for her by God (12:5–6). War breaks out in heaven between the archangel Michael and the Dragon. The Dragon and his angels are cast out of Heaven (12:7–12) but he then tries to persecute the Woman and her offspring (the Church) but ultimately fails (12:13–17). Then two great Beasts who serve the Dragon emerge from the Sea and the Earth. The children of the world follow the Beasts who control the crowds (13:1–5). The crowds who follow the beasts bear "the mark of the Beast", "666". But finally, the Lamb and the 144,000 "first fruits" who are redeemed are victorious over the Beast. The victory is followed-up with the "Seven Bowls" revelation. Seven angels are given a golden bowl, from the Four Living Creatures, that contains the seven last plagues bearing the wrath of God (15:6–8). Each bowl is poured out on the Beast and its followers (15:10–16:17–21). Then John sees a vision of the great Harlot, who sits on yet another Beast (with seven heads and ten horns, and names of blasphemy all over its body) (17:1–18), but her New Babylon is destroyed (18:1–8).

A new dawn begins with the Marriage Supper of the Lamb (19:7–10) and the Judgment of the great Beasts, the Dragon, and the Dead (19:11–20:15). The Dragon is imprisoned in the Bottomless Pit for a thousand years (20:1–3) but is then released and goes out to deceive the nations in the four corners of the Earth—Gog and Magog—and gathers them for final battle. The Dragon is defeated (20:7–9), and the last judgment ensues. John then sees a "new heaven" and "new earth" where there is no more suffering or death (21:1–8). God comes to dwell with humanity in the New Jerusalem (21:2–8).

Despite all of the fantastic imagery presented in the *Book of Revelation* its substantive message is clear: there is a battle going on between supernatural forces over the souls of men and the Earth. The Battle takes the form of a fight between two temporalities or ages: the age of wrath and the age of the new heaven and new earth. Jesus's intervention as the Lamb of God means definitive defeat for the anti-Christ and his allies and slaves. Those on the side of heaven are marked with the seal of God and those who are on the side of the Beast/Dragon are marked with the sign of the Beast. The former are distinct individuals while the latter move in crowds. The defeat of the anti-Christ's forces occurs after they are visited with a series of calamities. During the war those marked with the seal of God can navigate between the two ages and thus remain unharmed as there is safety in the new age.

How does one receive the seal of God and therefore the ability to cross through the gate into the new age and the new heaven and new earth? Presumably participating in the Christian community is a prerequisite to entry into the Kingdom, but in addition it seems reasonable to suppose that the author of the Book of visions wanted its listeners to become aware that there is a gate and that there are two ages and that there is a battle between the two ages. To wash one's robes in the blood of the lamb means many things but among these things it may indicate the ability to contemplate the dream-like images presented in the *Book of Revelation* to learn from them without losing one's sobriety or one's resistance to delusory nonsense. Listening to or reading the *Book of Revelation*, one gets a sense of the eschatological mood. It is future-oriented, foreboding, apocalyptic, visionary, and hopeful all at once and directed toward the End of Time. It is easy to see how so many people down through the ages used the images presented in these Revelations to justify the most delusory of hopes and the most criminal of deeds.

This is a dangerous book in the worst and best sense of that phrase. When its interpretation is left to individual febrile imaginings, who knows what its images can inspire? When, on the other hand, theologians seek to "interpret" it and thereby tame it, little of its wrath and horror is left. When interpreted in light of the great Christian tradition which includes the Church councils, the Church leaders, Doctors of the Church, theologians, and lay writers down through the centuries some of its power to unsettle remains even while the sails of those who wish to use it to pursue this-worldly utopian schemes at any cost are trimmed and reined-in to some extent. Its central message appears to be that Christians need to remain as pilgrims or wayfarers in this world. That we need to anchor ourselves in the hope of the world to come which Christ personifies. There is little in the Book to recommend compassion toward the current age. On the contrary the current age is depicted as the enemy that richly deserves the calamities poured out upon it by God and his angels. Nevertheless, compassion is a ferociously potent weapon in any war against demonic forces, so compassion and enmity are not necessarily opposed when it comes to the battle between the two ages. Thus, for the eschatological personalist the attitude has to be one of enmity, tempered by compassion, toward the current age and effort and love toward the coming age.

To explicate some of these themes concerning the two ages it is helpful to look at a couple of theologians who have made Revelation and the eschatological mood central to their work.

Eschatological mood in two theologians

Wolfhart Pannenberg[1] (1928–2014) has been described as a theologian of the *future as futurity* plays a central role in his theology. Pannenberg interprets the whole of reality in terms of the apocalyptic view of the world espoused by Jesus, St Paul, and most of the early Christian communities. Apocalypticism is pervaded by a mood of imminent revolution or the imminent violent irruption of a reckoning, judgment of the current age, and inauguration of something totally new. Pannenberg argued that we could arrive at the whole or the real or the truth only from a point of view of what we experience as the future or the sea of possibilities. If the Real is the Whole then we who are immersed in Time never fully grasp the real or the whole as everything is always changing and new things are constantly appearing and passing away. We have to wait until all things have completed their appearing to see or apprehend the Whole. We can only grasp the Real when the totality of things ceases evolving—when there are no new things under the Sun. We can only see the Whole from the End—thus the importance of the new Age when all will be revealed.

If we want to understand something we need to get at its essence. But given that the Whole is only revealed at the End time, each thing's (including persons) real essence exists as anticipation of its future essence. The bridge between the future and the present is the concept of *anticipation* or *prolepsis*. Indeed, eschatology and anticipation are correlative terms. The new age of the Kingdom of God, essentially an eschatological reality, has already come *proleptically*. The resurrection of the dead is an eschatological event, but it is anticipated or proleptically present in the resurrection of Jesus. What things (including persons) are is the anticipation of the completion of their process of becoming, that is, of their history. Thus, we enter the new age via anticipation, faith, and hope. From a personalist point of view, Pannenberg can be criticized as he seems unaware that the agent intellect in each individual is an uncaused, wholly completed unity. Its full nature may not be revealed till the End time, but that is not due to the fact that the agent intellect is not yet completed. It is due to our limited ability to see the real and the whole due to sin and error.

Like Pannenberg, Hans Urs von Balthasar (1905–1988)[2] was a theologian who exemplified both the strengths and weaknesses of adopting an eschatological take on all the major topics in Christian theology. Von Balthasar took one of the tenets of eschatological personalism very seriously when he began to use the data obtained from dreams and visions in his theology. Specifically, he allowed himself to be inspired by the dreams and visions of Adrienne von Speyr (1902–1967) who was a Swiss medical doctor and mystic. Perhaps because of this sensitivity to visions, dreams, and images, he made the transcendentals, particularly beauty, central to his entire theology.

One of von Balthasar's first works was a study of the role of eschatologically informed thought in German culture and philosophy of the 18th and 19th centuries. He reviewed the ways in which German intellectuals from the enlightenment up to the modern age struggled with commitments to the current age versus the age to come. They tended to over-value the current age via immanentizing the eschaton. We all want to adopt a fair estimate of the current age: we want to better our societies, fight injustice, and create harmony and cooperation. But these laudable efforts very easily slip into the extremes of utopian totalizing schemes that aim to revolutionize society from the bottom up—to make history intelligible and manageable, to tame its unpredictable character. Citizens in such utopian societies are not only required not to oppose the utopian schemes but they are not allowed to think against these projects and thus the political projects take on a religious fervor and totalitarian character. Eschatology gets inverted or immanentized in political form and thus deformed.

The true eschatological cannot be tamed or immanentized by man. The eschaton is not, as Hegel and Marx believed, the end of the historical because it is not part of history at all. The eschatological is the in-breaking into history of the eternal as manifested in the life, death, and resurrection of Jesus Christ. What breaks into history is not some abstract eternal realm but the person of Jesus. *The personal is the eschaton.* To the extent then that we realize the personal we are moving into the eschaton. Personalism must be eschatological. Christ inaugurated a new creation that grows within or underneath or beside history and therefore human history is gradually redeemed by and in Christ.

Von Balthasar's special contribution to eschatology is often said to be his doctrine of Holy Saturday. Basing himself partially upon the dreams and visions of Adrienne von Speyr, Balthasar argued that between his death and resurrection (during "Holy Saturday") Jesus utterly emptied himself of the Godhead and descended into Hell, thus redeeming all those who had been condemned to Hell. Apparently for von Balthasar we have grounds to hope that all may be redeemed; that no-one will suffer eternal damnation.

This of course is a key eschatological question: what is the ultimate destiny of each human being? Where is it all going? If persons count, if they have infinite dignity then they should have a real say in where it is all going? That freedom to help determine where it is all going also entails responsibility for rebellion concerning where it is all going. But should an individual with infinite dignity be condemned to everlasting suffering because he dissents as to where God wants to take the world? If a person can ultimately do no wrong and suffer no real consequences for his actions, then he has no real ontological weight. On the other hand, having a person with infinite dignity suffer eternal consequences for his actions brings into question that person's real ontological weight and freedom. It seems both eschatological options destroy personality: universal salvation does so by vitiating consequences of human actions (no-one can ever really get hurt) while the doctrine of everlasting damnation vitiates consequences of human actions by implying that some human choices and actions reverberate eternally. If some effect never ceases, never goes away then our choices don't matter because nothing can ever be lost. But freedom requires that choices can always be revoked.

It seems you cannot have universal salvation and retain freedom. Nor can you have eternal damnation and retain freedom. Here I am no longer summarizing Balthasar but instead explicating eschatological personalism. So the eschaton, the coming of the Kingdom of God cannot mean either of these two options. There will neither be universal salvation, nor eternal damnation. Then what? What picture of the Parousia, the coming Kingdom of God is compatible with both Freedom and the scriptural witness? If the eschaton is essentially a revelation of the Person of Christ then the only decision that counts is do I want to enter into relation with this person? Those that want to accept the collaboration will go on an adventure with Christ. Those that do not accept the invitation will finish out their lives and then be nihilated—they have received their reward while alive (Matthew 6:2–16; Luke 6:24) in whatever comfort and joy they gathered during their lives. Their forfeiture of the eternal adventure with Christ could be construed as a kind of hellish choice, but annihilation is what they chose and what they ultimately received—no further suffering. But what about individuals who intentionally do harm or criminal atrocities? Some post-judgment punishment seems just. Eternal punishment though? Can there be eternal consequences of an action? Not if we think of the person as a free agent. Freedom is incompatible with unceasing effects of an action. Therefore, eschatological personalism is consistent with Von Balthasar's position on the doctrine of Hell. On the other hand a person can "freely" choose to remain in hell and do so indefinitely. In that sense eternal damnation is possible.

To opt for the person of Jesus, for the coming Age, we need to orient toward the transcendentals. Balthasar argues that all of creation is capable of bearing witness to divine beauty, goodness, and truth. The human being's free agent intellect is enlightened by the analogous light of the transcendentals, which point to the absolute. Because the transcendentals are co-extensive with being as a whole they enlighten being as a whole, as well as its source and goal, God. This analogical power is possible because the transcendentals are not categories. The agent intellect, furthermore, is capable of grasping the immanent, unique qualities or form of a thing or individual. Grasping the particular and the unique in another person makes possible love. For Aristotle and Aquinas, form is grasped through the process of abstraction and formation of universals. For Balthasar (and Duns Scotus), on the other hand, the agent intellect can not only strip away qualities to arrive at the universal but in addition can unveil, find, or ascribe/add those particular qualities that make the individual uniquely who he or she truly is and thus love them for who they are. Borrowing from Goethe, Balthasar called the thing that makes something uniquely what it is Gestalt.

Gestalt or uniqueness contains an element of "futurity" in its being, a direction within its present making its existence essentially open-ended and pointing to an excess, intensification, or overflowing of itself. It is an ongoing unveiling or creativity. It continuously takes on qualities given to it by other agent intellects and by its own introspective activity (the agent intellect can reflect upon itself). This self-reflection creates an interior, private domain filled with qualia of all kinds and which Brightman called the shining present. But the agent intellect is also always overflowing and directed outward toward other persons and things in the world. It is essentially a polarity of interiority and communication, immanence, and transcendence. That open-ness to another is ultimately an open-ness and movement toward God. The movement of the finite creature to its ultimate fulfillment in God is also a movement to its idea which is its truth. To "become what you are" involves the gradual assimilation of the finite creature to its idea. The perfection of the finite creature consists not in its dissolution in the infinite but in the confirmation and strengthening of its limit, which, in turn, is done by maintaining a balance within its inherent polarity, a balance between immanence and transcendence, the current age and the coming age.

How do we maintain the balance between the current age and the coming age, immanence and transcendence, singularity versus the whole, and the human and the divine? For Balthasar balance is found via the analogy of "participation" or Przywara's *analogia entis*[3] wherein the human participates in God's divine life but can never match it fully. There is thus a similarity to God but it is strictly limited such that no matter what degree of similarity we attain, there will always be an infinitely larger dissimilarity between us. This "similarity in difference" relationship we have with God, furthermore, is dynamic and always changing. We can get better and better at becoming like God but we will never reach an end to that process. Our happiness is to become more and more like God and we can do that forever more...but we will never reach the end of that happiness. The similarity within an ever greater dis-similarity captures the right sort of balance between man and God such that there is no danger of ultimate dissolution of the individual into the whole. Nor is there the opposite danger of experiencing no connection at all to the divine. Instead the connection is real and capable of intensifying to an infinite degree.

When God creates a person it is not done *ex nihilo*. Rather he creates persons from out of his ideas. But these ideas are not identical with God's being (which is actuality). Instead, the ideas express the polarity inherent in the *analogia entis*, that is, the actualization of the idea involves the pouring out or emptying of the idea of its entire content so that there is a distinction between God and the idea. Yet because the kenotic process involved in the creation of the person started within the Godhead there is some remaining participation in the Being of God. Thus, the individual person is both similar to but infinitely dis-similar to God. Similarly, we can navigate successfully between the age of wrath and the coming age via the *analogia entis*. That is, there is a similarity between the two ages within an ever greater dis-similarity between the two ages. They are both populated by free persons for example. But the persons in the coming age will come into their full powers as free creative persons with resurrection bodies and so forth. We as individuals express a similarity in ourselves within both ages but there is a greater dis-similarity in our personalities between the two ages. The aim is to become more and more identified with, and anchored in the coming age.

Both Pannenberg and von Balthasar clearly evidence awareness of the two forms of temporality, the two Ages the eschatological Christian must navigate. This view of temporality supersedes conventional notions of time, but is it reasonable?

The unreality of time

Philosophers and scientists are beginning to sound like the theologians who argue for the unreality of clock time as well as the amazing variety of differing forms of temporal experience. The temporal structure of NOW is composed of a shining present, an immediately receding illuminating absent or past, and an immediately arriving future. But time, and certainly temporal experience, is not monolithic. It may be the case that there is more than one type of time. The information we obtain about temporal phenomena comes to us in the form of varying types of temporal experiences such as duration, clock time, time as understood within relativity theory and within quantum theory, everyday observations of the ordered succession of items and sequential processing of items in our cognitive systems, recall of memories, and anticipatory simulations of future states of affairs. Are our everyday experiences of duration or memory recall tapping the same temporal phenomena that is studied as time in relativity theory or quantum mechanics? Is time out there some objective substance composed perhaps of temporal particles? Or is time inextricably tied to our subjective perceptions? Or is there perhaps many types of time some of which underwrite quantum phenomena and some of which underlie subjective experiences; and can we navigate between the different forms of temporal experience?

We cannot here solve all the puzzles associated with time, never mind decide upon the basic issue concerning the metaphysical status of temporal experiences. For purposes of understanding the role of time in constituting personhood, I bracket decisions and speculations concerning the ultimate metaphysical status of time and assume simply that temporal experience indexes something real for the individual. We cannot yet definitively say what that something ultimately is but the fact that temporal experience indexes something real cannot be denied. In my discussions of the links between temporal experience and personhood the only assumption I make is that temporal experience indexes something real and that something real will ultimately be discovered by theological and scientific investigations.

When considering temporal experiences, it immediately emerges that there are a number of different "times" or temporal substances or temporal phenomena. The question therefore arises as to whether there is a temporal mode that is to be preferred over others and whether there is a temporal mode special to subjectivity and persons. Such a mode would occur only within subjectivity and may help to constitute experiences of persons. A personal temporality must also attempt to account for the experience of flow, of the experience that events come from the future, become present, and then fade into the past. Experiences "come from" the future. They "arrive" at an indexically fixed-point that Brightman called the shining present and we experience as our subjective presents or nows. But if the subjective present is really the experience of just arriving futures, the subjective present, and the unity in consciousness associated with it, is rooted in what we call the future. But the future, in turn, is really just the realization of possibilities, the coming into being of possibilities via the agent intellect.

Thus, in one sense these arrivals from the future are the actualizations of possibilities. Personal temporality is composed of a triadic structure (past, present, future). This triadic structure however is embedded in a consciousness that has a cumulative store of experiences that continuously grows with time such that the events that fade into the past do so into a continuously growing "past". But this illuminating absent can become a means for a turning back toward God. It can be redemptive. Even in the fallen state, persons remain essentially free. That freedom gives an individual the power of self-conscious appropriation of its past and future temporal modes. In appropriating its past the agent intellect or personal constitutes an enduring entity; in appropriating future possibilities the personal constitutes it distinctive project. The person stuck in time can nevertheless assert his freedom, his true person, the one who is rooted in the eternal to range freely over his entire subjective experience (past, present, and potential future) and re-interpret it, extract meaning from it, thus transcending the present and past. This interpretative activity underwrites redemptive narratives and underlines the importance of narrative in capturing the free component of the person.

Freedom and the power of narrative re-interpretation therefore demonstrate the subordination of time to the free person. In that personal sense time is illusory. The person merely needs to re-assert his true identity as free creative spirit to activate this interpretative activity and thus modulate the meaning of time itself for his personal life project. The ability to extract meaning and assert purpose demonstrates the fundamental malleability and unreality of time relative to the personal. Time's fundamental unreality also demonstrates that subjective experience will be dramatically different when persons are rightly oriented to God, when time drops away or dissolves like the illusion it is when the eschaton arrives.

The philosophy of time also points to the unreality of time. It takes its start from the science of time. Physics seems to suggest that time as flow is not observed among the physical phenomena studied by physicists. Instead, change is generally assimilated to entropy or increasing disorder within a closed system. Now it is not universally agreed that physics has no place for time as flow. Nor is the universe universally considered a closed system, so these preliminary and all too simplified summaries of what science tells us about time will very likely need to be adjusted in the near future.

There is a group of philosophers who argue that time is illusory. Time as flow, known as the A-series after McTaggart's original exposition,[4] can be reduced to time as static or the everlasting NOW known as the B series. The A series refers to time as commonly understood with a future arriving at a present that then recedes into the past and so forth. The B series by contrast refers to ordered relations between events that remain the same regardless of temporal reference. Event A occurs before event B regardless of what time it is for example. Within the A series camp, i.e. those philosophers who believe time as flow is real and not reducible to the B series, there are also a variety of positions concerning the nature of time. Some philosophers believe that only the present is real. The past is gone and the future is not yet. These are the presentists. Other philosophers believe that the present is specious and fleeting but give more weight to the past. Still others known as possibilists believe the past and present are real, but the future is not. "Eternalists" believe that all three modes, i.e. past, present, and future, are real. All three modes need to be real in order to establish truth-making ground for propositions that refer to the past and future. To claim that Napoleon was defeated at Waterloo is true if the past is real but cannot be established as true if you do not believe the past has any ontological reality or weight. But what about the future? If we hold with the eternalists that the future is real does that mean that future facts are already established? If so what becomes of human freedom?

We experience time as exhibiting an inherent direction. We remember the past but not the future. Past facts are fixed but causes typically have their effects in the future. B series advocates argue that satisfactory truth-maker conditions cannot be established for A series statements without falling into an infinite regress. These theorists offer instead a model of a block universe where time does not flow but is instead a relative phenomenon consistent with relativity theory and based solely on relational propositions like before and after. The idea is that every single event throughout the entire history of the universe exists and is individuated on the basis of these tenseless relational propositions. But the block universe view has no adequate account for the subjective experience of temporal flow.

Nor have A series theorists yet found a way to adequately ground temporal experiences. Therefore, a number of hybrid accounts of time involving both A and B series views have sprung up, all arguing that there is no in principle reason for not combining the two views to get a fuller picture of temporal phenomena. Lynne Rudder Baker (2010)[5] for example proposes a BA-theory of time in which A series facts refer to the experiences of self-conscious persons and B-series facts as observed by physics. The fact that A series facts are "mind-dependent" does not in any way for Baker diminish their metaphysical status as real entities. After all minds are real too! Robert Neville draws on the riches of process philosophical approaches to time as prehension and concrescence to develop an original theory of time. Neville[6] argues that temporality consists of an elimination of uncertainty and "vagueness" by working a plurality of conditions into a definite harmony. A strength of Neville's account is that the development of an enduring temporally thick "discursive actuality" occurs via cumulation of past achieved structure in harmonizing conditional and other features into new harmonies. He moves beyond process philosophy by providing an alternative account of enduring identity to that provided by process philosophy. For process philosophy enduring identity was established via mere causal reiteration of a similar pattern through a sequence of actual occasions. Neville notes that this account only provides a general persistence not a persistence for a specific individual. A reasonable account of the haecceity of an individual cannot be achieved via successive prehensions of previous occasions. What is needed is a unique sequence of cumulation of achieved structure and new values into new harmonies. The trajectory of an actuality achieves its haecceity via cumulation of past values as well as successive realizations of future normative possibilities that are objectively present as possibilities in the individual's world. Becoming inheres in the present moment, which, in turn, has present and future constituents that are inter-related and social. Similarly the structuring of the past and interpretation of the future are both learned from socially developed structures and social artifacts such as signs and symbols and thus each carries specific value and normative obligations for the individual.

Robert John Russell[7] draws on some of the theologian's Wolfhart Pannenberg's conception of eternity as the life of the trinity as mutual indwelling of the three persons or omnipresence of each in the other's person. For Pannenberg the future creation initiated by Christ reaches back into present creation to transform it in every respect and this is called prolepsis. Eternity for Pannenberg is not timelessness, nor endless time but really duration with specific internal structure that Russell calls "copresence". Duration in this view is a differentiated unity that holds together as co-present all events in the history of creation. Each event retains its unique past and future (Russell calls this time's "present-past-future structure" or ppf structure) and all events are held together simultaneously as distinct entities.

The phenomenologist Husserl[8] also described a tripartite form of temporality. According to Husserl the basic unit of temporality is not a "specious present" but a slightly longer block of duration that encompasses three modes of presentation to awareness. Awareness encompasses a primal presentation or present and a just receding pastness as well as a just arriving future. Retention is the component that allows us to be conscious of the just elapsed phase of the immediate now, while a protention intends the phase of the just arriving event/object. The full structure of temporality is protention-primal-retention. This structure is dynamic and always cumulating information as each new piece of information modifies the set of information currently in the durational pulse.

For the eschatological personalism I am presenting here, time in the "current age" is the form experience takes when we attempt to actualize possibilities without God's participation or collaboration. It is the result of our attempts at realization of possibilities outside of the will of God. Because we are not in full collaboration with God our creations are not ordered according to the transcendentals but are, instead, semi-random and ceaseless. The things we attempt to actualize never fully come into Being or actuality. Instead they persist in a progressively increasing disordered state in-between the actual and the potential I call the liminal realm and that physics calls "entropy". They are constantly manifesting or appearing because our selections from the realm of possibilities are not ordered rationally according to the transcendentals. Instead of enriching us, our experiences all too often burden us in the form of negative memories, or current worries and concerns. If we ordered our selection from the possible via guidance from the transcendentals (i.e. via rationality), we would experience hope rather than ceaseless concern and worry, joy rather than despair, and anticipation/optimism rather than gloom and dread over prospects for the future. In that case our experience of temporality would be eschatological. It would be anticipatory, hopeful, and intentional.

In absence of guidance from the transcendentals however, our experience of temporality would be mechanical and clock-like. In the liminal realm our actualizations of possibilities are biased in terms of things that increase our power over nature and over others, i.e. we constantly attempt to actualize the knowledge that allows us to build groups, tools, weapons, and machines. Because the things that increase power are few in number, we tend to attempt to actualize these same few behaviors, things, groups, and machines over and over again. We get stuck in a perseverative loop, i.e. we require more and more effort to realize fewer and fewer returns in terms of power. Our worlds start shrinking instead of expanding. We become proficient at producing things that produce power: groups (crowds) and machines. We come more and more to depend on the machines.

As Heidegger and Junger have taught us, however, the presencing of knowledge related to the machine puts us into an existential stance of "standing reserve" or subordination to the machine. We relinquish pieces of our autarchy every time we produce knowledge designed to control others in the absence of the guiding transcendentals. The subjective experience of temporality in the liminal versus the eschatological realm is therefore also colored by this sense of relentless necessity; of coercion coming from without; of slavery, subordination, and alienation from the true, the good, and the beautiful as well as autarchy or self-rule.

In the liminal realm therefore temporality colors the sense of self and subjectivity. There is an immense philosophical literature on the relation of personal identity and time. As far as I can tell, there are three general hypotheses on what confers identity over time: (1) psychological states, (2) bodily factors, and (3) "temporal parts". The psychological approach suggests that the unity we experience across time is due to psychological states like memory or intentional states or sense of purpose or more abstract states like the relations between consecutive psychological states or causal history between successive psychological states and so forth. Many authors have pointed to fundamental problems associated with the psychological approach. Among these problems is that all the purported psychological states hypothesized to ground identity involve breaks in continuity over time such as in deep unconscious sleep states or anesthesiology or vegetative states and so forth. Thought experiments involve so-called fission states where one hemisphere of the brain of an individual is implanted into one body, and the other hemisphere is implanted into a second body, with each carrying some psychological states of the original individual. So it is unclear which hemisphere grounds the personal identity of the person undergoing the transplants. These same thought experiments have also prompted some philosophers to argue that it is not personal identity per se that we care about but that some of "our" psychological states persist post fission. Many other philosophers do not agree with this intuition. Instead they argue that it certainly does matter where the "I" winds up as it is that "I" that will be able to link current states (sufferings, desires, etc.) with past history. There cannot be two "I"s doing that linking. Therefore the thing that grounds identity cannot be psychological states alone. Similar problems beset the bodily states criterion. Brute physical continuity cannot handle the fission/transplant cases. Nor does the "I" change in tandem with changes in physical state. The temporal parts hypothesis suggests persons are composed of a huge collection of time-defined parts that extend across a lifetime and that for every period of time when you exist, short or long, there is a temporal part of you that exists only then. The problem with the temporal parts view appears to be that it really does not solve the unity problem. Is the person the composite whole of all his or her temporal parts? If so how should we construe each temporal part? Is each part you? If not how do "you" persist from state to state if the whole does not change but only a small collection of parts change? If you do change with any change in temporal part then identity becomes unstable. This gives us many likely candidates for being you.

From an eschatological personalist view, a person in his unity is a whole without parts but the whole is not composed of some immaterial soul. Instead the whole person is anchored in the agent intellect (and ultimately the resurrected state) which is outside of time. Ultimately the Christian with eschatological hope is anchored in a "future" resurrection body-mind whole when Time ends and the Kingdom of God arrives. Continuity and unity over time are due to the fact that the person is a basic, bedrock, immutable entity in the universe. A person is a realization of an idea in the Mind of God, an independent agent intellect capable of bringing new worlds into existence. The person's essence therefore is wholly actual and eternal, and lies outside of time. A person is a center of free creative activity that, like

God, brings possibles into being and that creative activity is eternal as long as the person chooses to collaborate with God. When collaboration is refused the person falls into time and his subjective experience is marked by the temporal but the person's essence remains immutable and rooted in the eternal.

Despite being rooted in the eternal or the age to come the personalist must nevertheless learn to navigate between the two ages. He cannot lean too heavily on the coming age or transcendence as he would lose his way in the current age. Nor can he lean too much on the current age or immanence as he would end up accommodating himself to the current age. Navigation through the portal between these two ages is thus a delicate balancing act. We can learn about this balancing act by studying the portal between the two ages.

Eschatological dream-time

Where did those images and visions concerning the two ages in the *Book of Revelation* come from? From whence came those extraordinary images concerning the provisional nature of Time and two warring ages, the lamb with a sword in the mouth, the "one like a son of man", the throne, the woman clothed with the Sun, insects with metal-like bodies, beasts whose bodies are covered in eyes, etc. From a believer's perspective the answer would have to be from God. But God's messages are heard and received by the human mind/brain. In the case of visions like those in the *Book of Revelation* the mind/brain system most often implicated as a generative source of these sorts of images is rapid eye movement (REM) sleep, i.e. the dreaming brain/Mind. The dreaming and visioning mind/brain may play a role then in mentally balancing or switching between the two ages.

The popular conception that dreams reveal a less-censored or filtered portion of our consciousness is partially true—though dreams are also drenched in obscure symbols as well. In dreams we witness the actual cognitive process of actualization of possible worlds as well as visits to, and communications with alternate possible worlds. Even though dreams can give us a portal into the actualization process it is always partial as if seeing through a glass darkly and we seem never able to witness completion of the actualization process. The images are all coming into being but have not yet completed actualizing. Thus, like us they are settling into the liminal realm though they are not yet conditioned by Time. So they have a liminal, fleeting but timeless feel to them. Thus, some dreams, and nightmares, show us what we are constantly and compulsively working to realize out of the realm of possibilities when we do not consistently collaborate with God. Most dreams are unpleasant, but some dreams are pleasant, inspiring, awesome, and prophetic. These are the dreams we have when we use the transcendentals to guide us in realizing possible worlds. All religious traditions have developed criteria for discerning which dreams are "from God" and which are not. Those that are from God leave the dreamer feeling excited, hopeful, and better able to love. When the dreams are prophetic, they leave the dreamer inspired, awe-struck, and called to a higher ideal, an ideal that builds up human communities and makes the dreamer better able to love self and others. Dreams not from God are either emotionally neutral (not inspired by any particular spiritual entity) or demonic and nightmarish. These demonic nightmares represent a possibility or a possible world attempting to be realized that is monstrous from the human point of view. They are possibilities that should never be allowed into our world. Because dreams allow us to easily see which possibilities (good and bad) are being canvassed by the human mind as candidates for eventual realization or actualization, they are worth studying in greater depth.

Dreams have long been thought by ethnographers and anthropologists to be a key source for prophetic insights about the future as well as generation of cultural ideas, cultural myths, and collective memories. For example, a number of ethnographers and anthropologists have demonstrated beyond any reasonable doubt that traditional peoples used their dreams to speculate about the future or the age to come as well as to generate cultural and mythic ideas and collective memories.[9] Dreams have been empirically linked with several cognitive processes independently associated with future-oriented thinking and historical consciousness, such as narrative processing, mental simulation/time travel, facilitation of emotional memory consolidation, and counterfactual processing.[10] Indeed, dreams figure prominently in mythic, prophetic, and visionary experiences in all the world's religious traditions. I propose that dreams will be an important component of a full-bodied and robust eschatological personalism as they appear to be able to access alternate possibilities to this world as well as the timeless realm. This is the claim, as I see it, of the Christian tradition in any case.

In Acts 2:16–18 (New Revised Standard Version or NRSV), the apostle Peter addressed the crowds in Jerusalem after they had witnessed the early followers of Jesus speaking in tongues on the day of Pentecost. The crowds were awe-struck, fearful, and amazed, and so Peter explained to them what they were witnessing:

> [16] ...this is what was spoken through the prophet Joel:
> [17] 'In the last days it will be, God declares,
> that I will pour out my Spirit upon all flesh,
>   and your sons and your daughters shall prophesy,
> and your young men shall see visions,
>   and your old men shall dream dreams.
> [18] Even upon my slaves, both men and women,
>   in those days I will pour out my Spirit;
>   and they shall prophesy.

Peter appears to be claiming that we are in the "last days", and in the last days, God will pour out his spirit on everyone, slaves, men, women, old and young alike, and this will be manifest primarily in dreams and visions. Accordingly, for Christians, we must assume that we are in the historical period of "the last days". The old world is ending, and the new one is beginning. The new one is being heralded and born in dreams and visions so we need an eschatological personalism that incorporates dreams into its armamentarium to guide us through this historical period. Taking dreams seriously, though not uncritically, will be important to any eschatological personalism. Some dreams connect us to a pre-fallen paradisal state, our origins, and they prophetically connect us to the final End time state as well.

In the pre-fallen Garden of Eden Genesis 2:21 refers to Adam's sleep:

> [21] So the LORD God caused a deep sleep to fall upon the man, and he slept; then he took one of his ribs and closed up its place with flesh. [22] And the rib that the LORD God had taken from the man he made into a woman and brought her to the man.[23] Then the man said,

> "This at last is bone of my bones
>   and flesh of my flesh;
> this one shall be called Woman,
>   for out of Man this one was taken."

This text appears to show that sleep, and therefore dreaming, was a capacity for pre-Fall humanity. Sleep and dreams were a part of the paradisal state for human beings. Indeed, sleep gives rise to God's greatest gift to men: women. Though most dreams in the Old Testament (OT) appear in Genesis (Gen 20:1–18; 28:10–22; 31:10–14; 31:24; 37:5–8, 9–11; 40:5–19; 41:1–32), dreams and visions are referred to throughout the OT, and they serve a diverse array of narrative and theological functions.[11] For example, the dream scenes with Daniel and Nebuchadnezzar seemed to be patterned on the Joseph and Pharaoh interactions (Daniel 1:17 and 5:12). Like many other ancient persons King Nebuchadnezzar experienced his dream as a horrifying affliction, as a kind of possession state that required immediate and urgent treatment. That treatment could only be via valid dream interpretation—and only from a real dream specialist. He threatened to put to death all of the magicians, dream specialists, and wise men in his kingdom unless someone could immediately and validly interpret his dream. Thus, his unreasonable demand was that the contents of the dream be described to him first before the ritual interpretation event. He wanted apparently to validate the credentials of the dream specialist who would interpret his dream. Daniel then interprets the King's dream apocalyptically as a kind of revelation about the future course of world history as well as the end of the world when God will finally intervene for good. God thus reveals his plans for the world via a dream/vision. Eschatology appears to come to us via dreams/visions.

Besides the biblical accounts of prophetic and eschatological dreaming, there is now some scientific evidence that prophetic and precognitive dreaming may be real. Anecdotal claims of precognitive dreams are common, reported by 17–38% of survey participants.[12] There are many, very well-documented reports of people who claim to have had a dream that pictures, foretells, or depicts a scene or information that they later encounter in waking life. I find these anecdotal accounts of precognitive dreams compelling, but they have not received intensive investigation, so we know little about these dreams beyond the bare fact that people very frequently report them. It is possible to develop accounts of these dreams by explaining them away. For example, there is good evidence that the experience of "recognition" or "familiarity" or reminiscence can be de-coupled from actual memories of previous experiences so that you can get the experience of familiarity in contexts where familiarity should not occur. You are aware that the context is new for you so you ask yourself "why am I finding this scene familiar"? Then you confabulate an answer to the effect that you must have dreamt it. While the confabulation account surely explains some precognitive experiences, it does not really explain why the person reporting the experience believes it was dreamed. Why not confabulate some other story like it was a deja vu experience or retrieval of a partial memory, etc.? So such explanations are not fully satisfying.

Does experimental science tell us anything about precognitive dreams? Do people access the future or an alternate possible world in such dreams? Or are they merely confabulations? Krippner et al. (1968)[13] asked volunteers to look at a group of objects or scenes and told them that one of the objects would be selected to be displayed in the future and their task was to attempt to dream about the target that would be chosen to be displayed in the future. The next day the volunteers reported their dreams so there was no way the experimenters could unconsciously give away the target object to the volunteers as it had not yet been chosen. A random-number generator was used to select the target from the pool witnessed by the volunteer on the previous day. So, neither the volunteer nor the experimenter could possibly have known which object was chosen when the volunteers retired to bed to dream. The experimenters selected the target *only after* dream reporting was complete and submitted to the experimenters, *and before* the experimenters read the dream reports. Neither the dreamers, the experimenters, nor the independent judges (of dream report content) knew which target was selected before unsealing the dream reports. The task of the independent judges was to rate the similarity between dream content and the target. Hit rates (where dream content matched target content) in three out of four of these studies were statistically significant, suggesting that dreamers could experience dreams that contained content that significantly matched the target.[14] If you modify this basic experimental design a bit and allow the dreamer to view the target pool after they have reported their dreams and then have the dreamers rank the similarity of all of the items in the target pool against his or her own dream content, and finally have each dreamer submit a report of the contents of any dreams that occurred over five nights in which they attempted to focus on the target video, you get significant hit rates again.

While suggestive these experimental data concerning precognitive dreams remain ambiguous, given that some studies have failed to replicate these results. In the real world, however, people's daily experience seems to suggest pretty clearly that dreams seem able to access alternative worlds/ possibilities, and predict the future when it comes to a major life event. Take the case of the ultimate life event—the case of death. Death is one of those "last things" important in the theology of eschatology. Anecdotal accounts abound of dreams foretelling the death of a person but in this case we also have some quantitative data. Though seldom discussed in the scientific dream literature, dreams appear to have a special relationship to death and this relationship may reveal something about the power of dreams during emotional periods of a person's life. Two dream types are of especial importance with regard to death: (1) "visitation" dreams and (2) end of life dreams or dreams of the dying. With regard to #1 "visitation dreams" involve the bereaved being "visited" by a deceased someone they knew or loved. These visitation dreams are not experienced as mere dreams by the bereaved as many are utterly convinced that their deceased loved ones were really there with them in the room and that they touched, embraced, and communicated in the night. Equally importantly, these visitation dreams are therapeutically beneficial for the bereaved as they are comforted by the visitation. Back in 2014 Wright et al.[15] surveyed 278 bereaved persons regarding their dreams and found that 58% of respondents reported dreams of their deceased loved ones, with varying levels of frequency. Prevalent dream themes included pleasant past memories or experiences, the deceased free of illness, memories of the deceased's illness or time of death, the deceased in the afterlife appearing comfortable and at peace, and the deceased communicating a message (usually that they are OK). The respondents also noted that these visitation dreams increased acceptance of the loved one's death. We can regard these visitation dreams as the bereaved response to intense grief. Visions of the loved one were conjured from memory and made to serve the purpose of assuaging the grief of the dreamer. On the other hand, we can construe these dreams as authentic communications with another possible world—in this case the "afterlife".

With regard to end of life dreams (#2 above) this same group of researchers conducted a fascinating study on dreams of hospice patients.[16] What do people dream about when they are dying? These authors collected (and content analyzed) dreams from 59 hospice patients in roughly the 20 or so days before they died. Most (61%) of the patients were dying from cancer. The most common dreams featured friends or relatives of the dying patient who had died before them. These deceased persons conveyed a message to the dreamer that they were all going somewhere and that things would be OK. The appearance of these relatives in dreams was experienced as real or highly realistic, and the visitations were rated by the patients as a highly comforting experience. For example, Tim (age 51) had dreams that included his deceased parents, grandparents, and old friends who were "telling me I will be okay". "I haven't seen some of these people for years", he stated, and "I know we are going somewhere but don't know where". The authors stress the fact that their patients were not experiencing delirium or confusional states when they reported these dreams. Most interesting, as participants approached death, these realistic visitations and comforting dreams/visions of the deceased became more prevalent as death approached significantly predicting onset of death.

Thus, the deceased "visit" us after they die and later when we are facing death ourselves. In both instances the "visits" are experienced as real, not strangely or hallucinatory. Communication with the deceased occurs and the message is typically (though not invariably) comforting. In the process of dying these visits increase in frequency and intensity heralding death itself.

Why should dreams know about our impending deaths? One easy explanation that won't do is that dreams simply metaphorically reflect the dying body, so we directly intuit our deaths via feedback from our bodily organs. But there are many reports of dreams portending death when the individual was in the prime of life with no bodily illness. There may be something in dream neurobiology that allows dreams to develop very accurate predictions concerning the dreamer.

The eminent dream and brain researchers Allan Hobson and Karl Friston have called the dreaming brain a virtual reality machine[17] precisely in order to emphasize this capacity of the dreaming brain to simulate future possible states of the organism. Now of course the waking brain also performs simulations so it too is a predictive virtual reality machine that runs simulations of expected events all the time. But the waking brain uses differing sets of brain networks to run these simulations than does the dreaming brain. The theory formalizes a conception of the dreaming brain as a simulation machine or a virtual reality generator that seeks to optimally model and predict its waking state and environment, and needs REM sleep processes (particularly pontine geniculo occipital or PGO waves) to do so. The basic idea is that the brain comes genetically equipped with a neuronal system that generates a virtual reality simulation of the waking world during REM sleep because REM sleep processes are essential to optimize this generative model.

Treatments of the mind/brain as a virtual reality machine, a prediction error device, or a "Helmholtz machine" (all roughly the same thing) are rife throughout the cognitive and neurosciences, and it makes a lot of sense to consider dreaming along these lines as well. A dream, after all, is experienced as a partially realized possible "world" that appears to be generated internally without benefit of current sensory input (as sensory input is partially blocked during REM). Hobson and Friston suggest that sensory data are sampled during wakefulness to build up a complex model of the world that can guide behavior and reduce prediction error and surprises. Then the model is taken offline during sleep and is subjected to an optimization procedure that prunes redundancy and reduces complexity, thus improving the model's fit to the world.

During waking life changes in the model's parameters (experienced subjectively as percepts) are driven by the need to explain unpredicted visual input. During dreaming however, there is reduced visual or other sensory input so dreaming percepts are driven by the need to explain unpredicted oculomotor input. Dream content therefore is the brain's attempt to find plausible explanations for fictive visual searches of possibilities triggered by oculomotor input (via REMs and PGO waves presumably) and by the pruning of synaptic connections that is part of the complexity reduction optimization process.

REM sleep is the form of sleep most reliably associated with vivid dreaming.[18] Dreaming presents to us, in the form of dream images, the sea of possible worlds accessible to us and occasionally hones in on a single target world. It may be that some of the images in dreams are not under consideration for actual realization. These images may be just logically required relations to the images under active consideration for realization. But the emotionally charged images are very likely candidates for realization. Because the agent intellect is less active in dreams than in waking life these possible worlds are merely scanned and possibly tagged for later consideration by the agent intellect during waking life. Dream images however are not only composed of images produced by creatures but are also composed of images that reside in the Mind of God as they are ordered by the transcendentals. The theology and neurotheology of dreaming must be concerned with these dream images. We very likely experience them as somehow concerned with the future.

Now, during REM, the brain's reward system is intensely activated. Blocking dopamine (DA) release can decrease dreaming and administering dopaminergic drugs increases dream recall. Phasic DA release occurs during REM with some researchers claiming that this phasic DA release is the basis for hallucinatory wish fulfillment dreams. In association with this DA release there occurs a set of neural oscillatory activity or rhythmic patterns associated with future thinking in animals and humans. These are called theta rhythms. For example, hippocampal theta waves, with a frequency range of 6–10 Hz, appear when a rat is engaged in active, reward-seeking, exploratory behaviors and when planning future running routes through a maze. Theta waves frequently begin several hundred milliseconds before the onset of movement, suggesting they are associated with the intention to move. During REM, theta oscillations are present in both the hippocampus and amygdala and there is theta-rhythm coupling among CA1 of hippocampus, the amygdala, and medial prefrontal cortex or mPFC—all sites associated with creation of imaginative simulations about future options.

Interestingly brain mechanisms that produce REM theta and similar oscillatory states may also be implicated in temporal processing. One of the frequently discussed theories of temporal information processing is the striatal beat frequency theory. In the striatal beat frequency model, time experience itself is based upon the coincidence detection of oscillatory processes in corticolimbic-striatal circuits, the same circuits active during REM. In short, the process is conceived as a kind of binding process wherein coincidence detectors register the fact when several disparate oscillatory neuronal clusters oscillate in tandem or resonant. When that resonance occurs temporal information is registered and the subjective experience of NOW occurs. If, for example, a subject is asked to estimate the duration of an empty interval it is believed that at the onset of a to-be-timed signal, a phasic DA pulse from the striatum is triggered, DA is released, and its targets are neurons in cortical and thalamic sites. Striatal output travels via circuits in the basal ganglia to the thalamus and ultimately cortical sites along two pathways: the direct (DA D1 receptor mediated) and indirect (DA D2 receptor mediated) then loop back to the cortex and striatum. Differential activity in the direct and indirect pathways of the limbic and basal ganglia systems may serve to start, stop, or reset the timing process. The initial DA pulse will facilitate or initiate resetting the phasic firing pulses of populations of cortical neurons so that they begin oscillating at their endogenous periodicities. Once these cortical ensembles are oscillating the medium spiny cells in the dopaminergic stratum will fire as they detect these oscillations. The striatal medium spiny cells will detect coincident activation of specific cortical oscillation patterns. Activation of these coincident detection mechanisms will then facilitate adjustment of corticostriatal synaptic weights such that the striatal spiny neurons become "tuned" to specific patterns of coincident oscillatory activity, with coincident oscillatory activity forming the basis of computation of varying periods of duration. Given that oscillatory cortical activity is inherently periodic with regular synchronous firing intervals (its period) and regular changes in systematic manner as a function of time (its phase), these cortical oscillatory patterns can represent time intervals. Switching time registers is essentially a matter of tuning oscillatory patterns at different frequencies.

The temporal sense can also be altered by disorders of various kinds and the mediating mechanism is likely to be down-regulation of brain oscillatory activity. Given the central role of mesolimbic, nigrostriatal, and mesocortical phasic DA release to the striatal beat frequency model of temporal processing, it is not surprising that disorders associated with aberrations in phasic DA signaling, such as Parkinson's Disease and schizophrenia, are associated with significant deficits in temporal processing as well as changes in REM sleep dreaming. When phasic DA signaling is aberrant problems in timing and time perception could arise due to failure in the synchronization of cortical oscillations or resetting of striatal spiny neuron membrane potentials or general lowering of background tonic DA levels regulating internal clock speed. Depletion of either phasic DA signaling or background tonic DA would result in a decrease in the rate of cortical oscillations and the coupling of striatal spiny neurons for coincident detection. If coincident detection patterns became aberrant then so too would temporal processing patterns of all kinds of information as is the case in schizophrenia.[19]

The brain and the future

The brain itself functions as a kind of device to pick up, process, and simulate information concerning the future. This view of the brain is formalized within the predictive processing framework (PPF)—the framework drawn upon by Friston and Hobson utilized to model REM dreaming as a virtual reality prediction machine. The basic idea behind PPF is that the brain operates as a kind of future-oriented, hypothesis-testing simulation machine. It produces simulations or predictions about what it expects the world to be like and then computes the degree to which those predictions are discrepant, given the reality presented to the senses. Simulations and predictions are essentially possibilities and are therefore the raw materials the agent intellect uses to bring possibilities into existence. Crucially for personalism theory, what constitutes subjective, first-person experience in PPF is precisely these simulations or predictions about reality as well as the match/mismatch error signal that occurs when sensory feedback is received within the system. Our subjective experiences are composed of the possibilities we canvas or search through when we are bringing some range of these possibilities into existence. The agent intellect produces these simulations by extracting intelligibles from objects in the world or via the actualization process wherein possible worlds are brought into the actual world. The simulations and the error signal index or represent the possible worlds. The ongoing goal for the brain is to take the error signal produced by the mismatch between the simulation/prediction and the actual sensory information received and then to minimize that error signal by producing better possible world realizations or simulations/predictions that match or harmonize with the actual world in the next cycle.

Note that PPF very straightforwardly implies that persons are future-oriented, meaning-seeking individuals. After all that is precisely what the PPF-informed picture of the brain implies. The brain is a prediction machine that actively seeks out information quantified as surprisal (or surprise) to confirm or dis-confirm current simulations or hypotheses. It cannot settle for any kind of information given in the environment—it looks for information that makes a difference to the current hypothesis; it looks for and needs meaningful information—information that says something about the future. These are the intelligibles the agent intellect extracts from objects in the world.

When we look at brain activation patterns associated with simulations and predictions as well as the processing of the error signal we see the same brain structures operative as were implicated in the striatal beat frequency model of temporal experience. DA signaling within this striatal-prefrontal network operates as a prediction error minimization process, consistent with PPF. DA signaling varies as a function of error signal within this system—it increases for example for unexpected rewards and decreases for expected rewards. DA innervates a broad swath of hierarchically organized structures within the frontal lobes. Brodmann Area 10 (BA10) is the key node in this set of structures within the frontal lobes that operate in a hierarchical manner. Cytoarchitectonic and genetic evidence of BA10 demonstrates that the lateral frontal pole represents a novel evolutionary development unique to humans only.

BA10 is at the end of a processing hierarchy, and thus it is integrative with respect to the information that flows into it from other regions in the hierarchy. Its output is to other supramodal regions of the cortex and very likely includes actual decisions made, intentions to act, and selection of actions and goals to implement intentions. Thus, executive control over both the processing of information and of actions occurs only via this BA10-anchored processing hierarchy. The processing hierarchy respects and reflects the anatomic organization of the PFC, whereby posterior and caudal frontal regions support control involving temporally proximate, concrete action representations, and the rostral and anterior PFC supports control involving temporally extended, abstract representations. As meaning-related cognitive content "moves" from posterior to anterior sites or from top to bottom regions, information or action commands become much less abstract and general and much more concrete and specific. Processing proceeds along a rostral-caudal axis in the lateral PFC, where more anterior regions represent the high-level abstract forms of goal representation and more posterior regions model progressively lower-level information as concrete motor and sensory data streams that implement action plans. A dominance relationship exists where anterior lateral PFC cognizes abstract, super-ordinate, domain-general rules and modulates the lower-level posterior lateral PFC domain-specific and subordinate areas. A hierarchical Bayesian system likely structures the flow of information processing, and DA-regulated frontostriatal circuits are fundamental to proper function of information exchange and processing along the chain of lower-level to higher-level hierarchies.

PPF is consistent with this striatal-prefrontal hierarchical processing system. Crucial to PPF is that the brain's predictions or simulations or hypotheses must be hierarchically organized, with the hypotheses of one level providing the inputs for the next level upstream and so on. "Higher" parts of the hierarchy are, roughly, those parts that are further away in time from the sensory stimulus. These tend to be at longer temporal timescales, and a higher level of abstraction. "Lower" parts of the hierarchy are closer to the sensory stimulus. These tend to be operating at shorter timescales, and at more concrete representational formats. According to the PPF, the brain's main task is to "infer" from incoming signals what the causes of those signals are. However, the incoming signal is always noisy, and more than one hypothesis is compatible with the incoming signal; thus, the brain needs to take into account both the fit of the input with the hypothesis, and the "prior probability" that that input would have occurred. Note that "prior probabilities" likely include all of the genetic information of the individual and all of the ecological-cultural information the individual has absorbed. If the simulation/hypothesis does a good job of predicting inputs, e.g. if it minimizes prediction error, it is kept. If it does a bad job, it is updated in favor of another hypothesis that does a better job.

Now crucially for personalist theory according to PPF, the only information that gets passed on up the cortical hierarchy is sensory information as encoded/captured in the *prediction error signal*. This stands in sharp contrast to the standard view of neuro-cognition according to which sensory information devoid of an error signal gets passed through the processing hierarchy which progressively gets transmitted to neocortex and then magically results in a unified experience. The fact that it is the error signal that carries the optimal information for brain/mind modeling of the world suggests that *we are built to compare what is to what we expect there to be and ultimately to what we think there ought to be,* and that therefore moral accounting is deeply engrained in brain and cognitive processing dynamics.

Now ethical commitment indicates a comparison between what is and what ought to be. In PPF terms that would entail (in very broad strokes) the brain producing a simulation of what its behavior ought to be and then using error signals to bring what actually is, into conformity with what ought to be. In psychological terms this might be construed as bringing a current self closer to a desired future self. That is the four-step decentering process I described in my 2009 book on religious experience.[20] The dopaminergic striatal-prefrontal hierarchical processing network described above would likely be a key brain network mediating this process. This network generates a simulation of the desired future self and initiates an active search for the kind of information that would assist the brain in adjusting its systems so as to better reduce the real distance between the current and future selves. It samples the world and its own behaviors so as to compute the distance between current and future selves. It sends this distance/error signal up the hierarchy so as to implement future behaviors that will reduce that distance next time around. The individual commits to a long-term struggle to achieve the goal of realizing the future self. This is a beginning of a start for development of an ethical stance as it aims at an "ought". The gradual reduction in distance between current and future selves results in a temporary reduction in the tension between current and future selves.

In the PPF the brain is seen as a prediction machine. It is constantly spinning out predictive simulations of what might be and what it expects to find and then testing these predictive simulations against what actually occurs. Now, if we conceive of future-oriented thinking as the process of creativity wherein we actualize possibilities, then we have to think of the brain not merely as a predictive machine but as a predictive machine that accesses the realm of possibilities and then selects some of those possibilities to be realized. Therefore the aim of the modeling process that the brain engages in is to realize those possibilities that are in process of being actualized. The brain models a world not as the world is but as the brain *would like it to be* (within the bounds of what sensory feedback reveals the world to actually be). The brain is a "future-accessing" machine, it is true, but it is more of a desire machine than a predictive machine. The predictive machine is there but it is subordinate to the desire machine or anti-machine as it is capricious and sometimes chaotic. The possibilities the desiring brain selects to be actualized are typically those that are latent within the realm of actually existing things. These latent possibilities are "potentially" existing things. They are compossible to what already exists. (When things come into being that have no relation to existing things, then these are called incompossible to actually existing things). Therefore the brain models what it desires the world to be; it wants the world to match its desires. It expresses and implements the free activity of the persons constrained by the reality of living in the liminal realm. The brain is not seeking to match the sensory information of what actually is. Instead it is seeking to actualize what the person wants the world to be. The person in the liminal realm wants to manifest knowledge or things that help him to attain power to dominate the world, rather than realize manifestation of the true, the good, and the beautiful. Now, control and domination is not always in contradiction to manifestation of the transcendentals—it just often is in contradiction. The brain is not merely attempting to produce the best most accurate models of the world as it is; it seeks to actualize those possibilities that will best allow it to control and transform that world so that world best accommodates the desires/possibilities being actualized. In the liminal realm the brain functions in a semi-random but biased manner as it favors the production of knowledge that serves the machine.

Given the PPF model and the idea of the brain as a prediction machine or a desire-oriented machine how does the REM dreaming system fit into that PPF framework? As mentioned above, Hobson and Friston suggested a view of REM within PPF that models the role of REM as offline adjustment of parameters of the PPF process model. But I would like to suggest that REM is the actual generator of models; it is the brain machine that produces the actual "simulations" (possible worlds), not just adjustment of its parameters.

REM produces a chemical environment in the brain that is similar to the effects produced by the ingestion of potent hallucinogenic drugs such as psilocybin—though of course at a much lower intensity level.[21] REM thus mimics, to some extent, a temporary, ecstasis or insanity.[22] During REM, serotonergic activity in the raphe and limbic sites is dramatically reduced, while dopaminergic and cholinergic activity is significantly enhanced in limbic sites. This chemical profile associated with REM is similar to what is produced by ingestion of hallucinogens. The brain during both REM and drug-induced hallucinogenic experiences seems to come under the influence of 5-hydroxytryptamine 2A or 5HT2A (serotoninergic) receptor signaling systems (more on that below). Complex interactions between the 5HT2A receptor signaling systems and other transmitter systems occur in prefrontal sites with the sensory association, limbic, amygdalar, and ventromedial prefrontal cortex intensely activated and the dorsolateral prefrontal cortex deactivated during both REM and "acid trips".

Psilocybin and other hallucinogenic drugs, such as lysergic acid diethylamide LSD, are known to reliably produce visions and spiritual experiences. Griffiths and colleagues have recently studied healthy volunteers who were given psilocybin or a stimulant/placebo (methylphenidate) and then observed in the lab.[23] Both experimenters and participants were blinded to who got what pill (double-blind procedure). Participants who were given the psilocybin evidenced higher (relative to the placebo group) scores on spirituality and mystical experiences scales. When the psilocybin participants were interviewed again 14 months later, 58% said they rated the experience they had on the drug as being among the five most personally meaningful of their lives, 67% said it was in their top five spiritual experiences. Griffiths et al. have recently shown that psilocybin-occasioned mystical and spiritual experiences are associated with long lasting positive changes in psychological functioning and in trait measures of prosocial attitudes and behaviors.[24]

Psilocybin is a naturally occurring tryptamine alkaloid with actions mediated primarily at serotonin 5-HT2A receptor sites. These receptors are located primarily in limbic and ventromedial prefrontal cortex.[25] 5HT2A receptor signaling, in turn, appears to be crucial to production of REM physiology. 5HT2A receptor sites have been found on cholinergic REM on-off neurons in the brainstem. Direct injection of agents (onto these REM on-off cells) that block or enhance 5HT2A signaling also changes the number of REM episodes the animal undergoes. The 5HT2A receptor, however, exerts its greatest pharmacologic effects on cortical functions. The receptor is found in great densities within the pyramidal projection neurons of the prefrontal cortex and the sensory association areas of the cortex—the very sites most activated in REM.

The most potent and common 5HT2A agonists are the so-called psychedelic drugs like psilocybin and LSD. Administration of these agents to human volunteers produces a variety of unusual perceptual phenomena as well as hallucinatory dream-like states. The most important effect of these drugs is sometimes called "ego dissolution"—a profound alteration in the sense of self and bodily boundaries. Ego dissolution can be a positive or a terrifying experience. In positive ego dissolution the individual lets go of a limited sense of self and identifies with an enriched sense of self. The intensity of the ego-dissolution experience predicts the magnitude of the perceptual and cognitive changes associated with the psychedelic experience. Kraehenmann et al. have demonstrated that the cognitive bizarreness (i.e. presence of improbable, impossible, or incongruent events during a given experience) common to both dreams and LSD experiences correlates with other aspects of the psychedelic experience, such as ego dissolution, and depends upon 5-HT2A receptor activation.[26] Ego dissolution and related experiences I submit are really just the dissolution of temporal frames for experience and the simultaneous activation of the agent intellect. The activation of 5HT2A receptors via dreaming or psychedelics dissolves the temporal frame within which we encounter the world in the liminal realm. Temporal function dissolves in the psychedelic state and partially in the dream state. We are taken out of the liminal realm and placed back into the timeless realm during these states. We can therefore access alternative worlds and are immersed in a sea of images or possibilities. But because the realm of the possible for persons in the liminal state is not consistently ordered by the transcendentals both psychedelic experiences and dreams can be both beautiful and horrific.

Functional brain imaging studies of the brain during REM have demonstrated a down-regulation of dorsolateral prefrontal, parietal, and supplementary motor cortex as well as an upregulation of limbic and sensory association cortex.[27] Functional brain changes under the influence of 5HT2A agonists have also been carefully studied with fMRI and other techniques.[28] 5HT2A agonists, like psilocybin and LSD, consistently produce an ensemble of brain changes that involve a global down-regulation of dorsolateral prefrontal (and perhaps parietal) activity and an upregulation of sensory association areas and limbic emotional areas. This profile of functional brain changes is remarkably similar to what occurs in REM sleep. The higher executive control systems centered in the dorsolateral prefrontal cortex are relaxed or actively inhibited while the sensory processing and emotional processing centers go into overdrive.[29] The influence of neural activity from lower-order sensory association and limbic regions upon higher-order regions is dramatically enhanced. Presumably, under these functional brain conditions, the integrative processing centers within the ventromedial prefrontal regions are inundated with very highly processed sensory information, thus allowing for production of a highly processed and unique form of information—a form of information that must involve very highly refined analyses on the significance of recent sensory and perceptual information.

Dreams have to be understood within the context of their links with "daydreams" and "visions". Components of REM can appear in partial form during waking life as in daydreams and "dreamy" states.[30] When

these REM irruptions last longer than a few seconds they are likely to produce more prolonged dreamy states and maybe even "visions". It is well
established that sleep deprivation reliably produces compensatory attempts
to enter REM throughout the day resulting in REM microsleeps as well
as reports of dreamy states and dissociative symptoms.[31] The role of sleep
mechanisms in the generation of visual hallucinations is well recognized in
narcolepsy in the case of hypnagogic hallucinations, which are thought to
derive from a REM-dissociation state in which dream imagery intrudes into
wakefulness. Van der Kloet, Merckelbach, Giesbrecht, Lynn, Mahowald,
Cramer Bornemann, and Schenck review a range of evidence that demonstrates that dissociative symptoms such as absorption, derealization, and
depersonalization, and other symptoms associated with a range of psychiatric disturbances originate from sleep.[32] REM intrusion has been reported
to contribute to psychotic symptoms, delusional states, and out-of-body
and Near Death experiences.[33] In short, REM neurobiology is at the root
of most dreams and most waking visionary states that occur during waking
periods. REM-related brain mechanisms produce highly refined analyses
on the significance of recent highly processed sensory information. Because
the dorsolateral prefrontal cortex is down regulated in REM these highly
refined analyses are relatively uncontrolled and free-wheeling so that more
disparate connections can be made between elements within the analyses[34]
(Cai et al., 2009). During REM we become more receptive to the significance of highly processed sensory impressions. Because the neurochemistry
of REM mimics to some extent the neurochemistry associated with hallucinogenic drugs the dreaming mind is acutely sensitive to the spiritual
significance of images and ideas. But note that the neurochemical profile of
REM involves far less of a "dose" of the neurochemical effect associated
with the classic hallucinogens. Therefore it would be false to claim that
REM dreaming is equivalent to an "acid trip". Nevertheless, the neurobiology of REM dreaming appears to promote meaning-seeking and visionary
experience.

If we concede that the neurobiology of REM does appear to consistently
and regularly reorganize higher cortical centers to enhance connectivity
between primary sensory center and higher-order cognitive processing
centers, then we have to ask how does the brain process this kind of content? We all know from experience that many dreams seem to make no
sense at all. They are bizarre and confusing. That is why many students
of dream phenomenology claim that dreams are like obscure texts that
need to be interpreted. Freud, of course, was the most famous of the dream
interpreters. White[35] has argued that historians unconsciously utilize the
four major stylistic tropes metaphor, metonymy, synecdoche, and irony
when analyzing obscure historical materials and attempting to make sense
out of the chaos that is history. To oversimplify White's rich tropological
philosophy of history, metaphor involves a comparison of materials with
something familiar. Metonymy involves breaking up those materials into

parts; synecdoche involves reorganizing those materials into a new whole, and irony involves reflection on that new whole. In 1999, White showed that these four tropes are effectively equivalent to Freud's dreamwork operations, such as displacement (metonymy), condensation (metaphor), presentation (synecdoche), and secondary revision (irony). We have to assume that when dreams access the "future" or place us into a sea of images that represent the possibles we may select for realization, the information in dreams needs to be decoded. Which images will be selected by the waking agent intellect for actualization into Being? White's tropology may be a first step in that decoding work. When the agent intellect selects an image or set of images/forms to bring into Being it must first foreground or highlight those images via comparison with other more familiar images (this is the metaphor stage) and then break up those images (metonymy) into parts that can be formatted for realization/actualization; and then reorganize them according to some value hierarchy ideally using the transcendentals (synecdoche). All of those operations occur in dreams. Then the highlighted and reformatted images are reflected upon during periods of daydreaming in waking life when REM temporarily intrudes into waking consciousness (here irony does its work) and then finally a selection is made as to what to bring to life. In short, in dreams we see the images/possibilities we are currently entertaining as candidates for realization. The dreamwork involves selection and reformatting a set of those images primed for realization. In waking life the agent intellect will make the final decision as to which images to bring into Being and store into long-term memory. Those images and memories then become the basis for the individual's sense of lived time or temporality. In the case of the eschatological personalist they become the basis for a sense of warring temporalities. One temporal line is filled with angst, care, and fear, and the other is filled with hope, anticipation, and excitement. The latter temporal line connects the individual up with a vision of the idealized Kingdom of God on Earth. If the individual commits to the Kingdom of God the first temporal line is gradually left behind as the individual begins to see it as fundamentally illusory.

Eschatological data: Marian apparitions

And there appeared a great wonder in heaven: a woman clothed with the sun, and the moon under her feet, and upon her head a crown of twelve stars. — Revelation 12:1

Unlike most philosophical or theological positions, the eschatological personalist values information obtained from dreams and visions, provided that that information has been demonstrated to meet certain discernment criteria. The key criterion is that the information enhances the spiritual well-being of the ecclesial community. But there is no denying that information from dreams and visions is notoriously unreliable and open to all kinds of arbitrary interpretations. The fact that eschatological personalism uses this kind of information therefore needs to be defended. I have done so to some extent above by showing that contrary to popular opinion, the dreaming brain is accessing highly processed information in the brain and that the content of dreams is less chaotic than widely assumed. I have also argued that the same brain physiology that is associated with dreams also informs daytime daydreams and visionary states. Therefore, dreams and visionary states are not always due to brain dysfunction or hallucinations. When the dreams or visions nudge people into healthy behaviors that are generally productive for the community then the dreams and visions are worth considering further. But this is not the only discernment criteria dreams and visions must meet before they can be used as data in eschato-logical personalism. Once hallucinations and destructive visions are ruled out the information must be demonstrated to not run counter to revealed and settled truths of Christianity. These are, broadly speaking, the tenets of the Nicene Creed. If the information has met all of these criteria then the eschatological personalist is free to attempt to interpret the information and to act on it.

Theologians, including Roman Catholic theologians, have been slow to appreciate the eschatological significance of Marian apparitions. There may be a generalized contempt directed at the seers of these visions given the fact that most have been unschooled, humble folk, children, house-wives, and nuns. The seers are typically individuals with no special training in theology, though their visions invariably speak to profound human and theological issues of the day. Church authorities, including local priests, bishops, and the magisterium, have likewise been consistently hostile to these visions, with the significant exception of several popes. The messages the Blessed Virgin Mary (BVM) delivers to the Church via the seers typ-ically involve apocalyptical themes of calling the Church and the world to repentance. There are warnings of imminent doom and chastisement if behaviors are not changed. There are judgments against the current age and a pointing to the coming blessed age.

It is somewhat odd that the Church and its theologians should be so adverse to Marian apparitions given the tremendous fruit these apparitions have borne for the faithful and the Church over the past two centuries. Look at Lourdes for example. It not only has consistently been associated with miraculous cures of chronic illnesses for many decades, it also helped to illuminate the theological significance of the doctrine of the immaculate conception. The doctrine was held by most of the Church since Late Antiq-uity, but was not dogmatically defined until 1854. Although there had been repeated attempts down through the centuries to have the doctrine defined as dogma it is generally agreed that the rise of Marian apparitions in the modern period (beginning after the French Revolution) put the doctrine firmly on the agenda of the magisterium who finally acted in the mid-19th century. Directly after the dogma was defined a 14-year-old girl, Berna-dette Soubirous, claimed that a beautiful woman appeared to her and said,

"I am the Immaculate Conception". The Church investigating the apparition years later confirmed it was the BVM and authentic. The BVM also
repeatedly urged the Church and the world to repentance just as she has
done at most of the other places she has appeared. Seen in an eschatological
light the doctrine of the immaculate conception (as well as the later defined
dogma of the bodily assumption of Mary into Heaven) suggests that both
the new Adam (Jesus) and the new Eve (BVM) have already inhabited their
resurrection bodies and inaugurated the new Heaven and the new Earth.
Both Eve and Adam triggered the Fall so it is fitting that a new Eve and
Adam inaugurate the new Age. Ordinary people apparently know this and
intuit it and then passionately strive toward its realization in visions. But
Lourdes is not the only apparition event that has carried eschatological
significance. Apocalyptic messages have been delivered at numerous contemporary apparition sites, including Guadalupe, Fatima and Medjugorje.

Eschatological messages have the capacity to inspire huge movements
among the laity. These apparition sites have become centers of devotion, at-
tracting millions of pilgrims each year. Approximately two million people
annually visit the shrine at Fatima, where apparitions of the Virgin Mary
appeared in 1917 to three illiterate children. Over five million individuals
visit Lourdes each year and 12 million people visit the Basilica of Our Lady
of Guadalupe near Mexico City, where the Virgin appeared in 1531 to Juan
Diego. At least a million people a year visit Medjugorje, Yugoslavia, one
of the more recent apparition sites. The Medjugorje visions began in 1981
with five teenagers and one child. The local Bishop and clergy developed
negative appraisals of the visions but Rome intervened deeming the bishop's
investigation inadequate. Rome appears to be favorably disposed to Medjugorje. The BVM's messages delivered via the seers have been consistently
apocalyptic in tone. There are constant admonitions to pray, fast, and go
to confession. One of the more dramatic messages is that there will be a
worldwide flash or illumination of conscience for each and every individual
in the world. It will reveal to each individual his or her sins and it will give
individuals a final chance at repentance before the coming judgment and
chastisement.

While academic theologians hold these Marian apparitions and warnings
in contempt, the eschatological personalist needs to take them seriously as
they can inform eschatological theory and practice if rightly considered and
studied.

We have now completed our survey of the key operating characteristics
of the agent intellect with respect to the eschatological dream time. Its activity constitutes the metaphysical basis of personhood. It operates on matter not the other way round and thus is superior to matter. Nothing in it
needs to be actualized. Instead it functions to actualize possibilities. Its key
phenomenological correlate is imaginative activity. It generates and operates on images. It realizes possible worlds and when it collaborates with
God the things or worlds it brings into reality are instances of the true,

the good, and the beautiful. When the agent intellect adds qualities to an intelligible form it has actualized it is specifying that thing's haecceity or uniqueness. When, on the other hand, the agent intellect abstracts qualities away from intelligible forms it has actualized it arrives at universals, the basis of generalized knowledge. When collaboration with God is refused the agent intellect operates under conditions of fallenness. It continues to actualize possibilities or intelligible forms but it does so without guidance from the transcendentals. The forms it then actualizes may not be beneficial to human beings. They are in any case subjected to futility and entropy. All the things we bring into being in the fallen state are subject to Time characterized by deterministic necessity and futility. The Christian revelation, however, reveals a different kind of time: one characterized by hope and freedom. These two temporalities are at war with one another in our hearts. The two temporalities are at war with one another but the eschatological personalist can safely inhabit both ages. He or she is given a "seal" that makes them able to pass through a portal between the ages with this portal being the experience of dreams and visions. We have systematically reviewed the neurobiology of dreams and visions and found that neurobiology to be consistent with the visionary functions assigned to it by eschatological personalism. We need now to describe the subjective experience of this war in order to complete our account of the agent intellect. We need a phenomenological description of how we experience the agent intellect, despite these warring temporalities. We need a phenomenological account of subjectivity.

Notes

1 The most complete statement of his views can be found in his Systematic Theology. W. Pannenberg. *Systematic Theology*. London: T and T Clark, 1988–1994.
2 I have not read all of Balthasar's works. I have relied on his *A Theological Anthropology*. New York: Sheed and Ward 1966 and his *The Glory of the Lord: A Theological Aesthetics*. Vol. 5, The Realm of Metaphysics in the Modem Age. Translated by Oliver Davies, Andrew Louth, John Saward and Martin Simon. San Francisco: Ignatius Press, 1991 as well as Nicholas J. Healy. *The Eschatology of Hans Urs von Balthasar*. Oxford: Oxford University Press, 2005.
3 Erich Przywara. *Analogia Entis. Metaphysics: Original Structure and Universal Rhythm*. Translated by John R. Betz and David Bentley Hart. Grand Rapids: Wm. B. Eerdmans Publishing, 1932/2014.
4 J. M. E. McTaggart. "The Unreality of Time." *Mind* 17: 457–473; reprinted in J. M. E. McTaggart. *The Nature of Existence*, Vol. 2, 1927. Cambridge: Cambridge University Press: Book 5, Chapter 33.
5 L. R. Baker. Naturalism and the First-Person Perspective. New York: Oxford University Press, 2013.
6 *Recovery of the Measure*. Volume 2 of the Axiology of Thinking. Albany: State University of New York Press, 1989.
7 Robert J. Russell. *Time in Eternity: Pannenberg, Physics, and Eschatology in Creative Mutual Interaction*. Notre Dame: University of Notre Dame Press, 2012.

8 My summary of Husserl's position relies on secondary sources primarily R. Sokolowski. *Introduction to Phenomenology.* New York: Cambridge University Press, 2000.

9 See, e.g., George Devereux. *Reality and Dream; Psychotherapy of a Plains Indian.* New York: International Universities Press, 1951; Dorothy Eggan. "The Significance of Dreams for Anthropological Research." *American Anthropologist* 51, no. 2 (1949): 177–198; Lee Irwin. *The Dream Seeker: Native American Visionary Traditions of the Great Plains.* Norman: University of Oklahoma Press, 1994; M. C. Jędrej and Rosalind Shaw. *Dreaming, Religion, and Society in Africa.* Studies on Religion in Africa, Vol. 7. Leiden; New York: E.J. Brill, 1992; Benjamin J. Kilborne. "Moroccan Dream Interpretation and Culturally Constituted Defense Mechanisms." *Ethos* 9, no. 4 (1981): 294–312; Waud H. Kracke. "Dreaming in Kagwahiv: Dream Beliefs and Their Psychic Uses in an Amazonian Culture." *Psychoanalytic Study of Society* 8 (1979): 119–171; Jackson Steward Lincoln. *The Dream in Primitive Cultures.* Oxford: Cresset Press, 1935; Barbara Tedlock. *Dreaming: Anthropological and Psychological Interpretations.* Santa Fe: School of American Research Press, 1992; Edward B. Tylor. *Primitive Culture.* London: Murray, 1873. Erika Bourguignon. "Dreams and Altered States of Consciousness in Anthropological Research." *Psychological Anthropology,* 1972, 403–434; Schenkman Publications; Roy G. D'Andrade. "Anthropological Studies of Dreams." *Psychological Anthropology: Approaches to Culture and Personality,* 1961, 296–332; Dorothy Eggan. "The Significance of Dreams for Anthropological Research." *American Anthropologist* 51, no. 2 (1949): 177–198; Dorothy Eggan. "Dream Analysis." *Studying Personality Cross-Culturally,* 1961, 551–557; Gustave Grunebaum and Roger Caillois. *The Dream and Human Societies.* Berkeley: University of California Press, 1966; Charles D. Laughlin. "Communing with the Gods: Consciousness, Culture and the Dreaming Brain." *Daily Grail,* 2011; Roger Ivar Lohmann. *Dream Travelers: Sleep Experiences and Culture in the Western Pacific.* New York: Palgrave Macmillan, 2003; Barbara Tedlock. *Dreaming: Anthropological and Psychological Interpretations.* Santa Fe: School of American Research Press, 1992.

10 For review see P. McNamara. *Neuroscience of Sleep and Dreams.* Cambridge: Cambridge University Press, 2019.

11 Shaul Bar. *A Letter That Has Not Been Read.* Translated by Lenn J. Schramm and Robert Karl Gnuse. *The Dream Theophany of Samuel: Its Structure in Relation to Ancient Near Eastern Dreams and Its Theological Significance.* Lanham: University Press of America, 1984; Marina Hofman. *Dream Type-Scene in Old Testament Narratives: Structure and Significance,* ProQuest Dissertations and Theses, 2015; Jean-Marie Husser. *Dreams and Dream Narratives in the Biblical World.* Sheffield: Sheffield Academic Press, 1996; David Hymes. "Toward an Old Testament Theology of Dreams and Visions from a Pentecostal-Charismatic Perspective." *Australasian Pentecostal Studies* (2012), Retrieved from https://aps-journal.com/index.php/APS/article/view/117; Diana Lipton. "Revisions of the Night: Politics and Promises in the Patriarchal Dreams of Genesis." London: Sheffield Academic Press; 1 edition (1999); Benjamin Pate. *An Examination of Dream Narratives as Divine Revelation in the Old Testament Canon: Recipient, Message, and Response,* ProQuest Dissertations and Theses, 2015.

12 Lange, R., Schredl, M., & Houran, J. (2000). "What precognitive dreams are made of: The nonlinear dynamics of tolerance of ambiguity, dream recall, and paranormal belief." *Dynamic Psychology: An International Interdisciplinary Journal of Complex Mental Processes.* (http://www.goertzel.org/dynapsyc/dynacon.html); Parra, A. (2013). "Phenomenological examination of premonition

experiences in dreams and waking states: A survey study." *Australian Journal of Parapsychology*, 13, 187–212

13 S. Krippner. "Experiments in Telepathy." *The Journal of the American Society of Psychosomatic Dentistry and Medicine* 15, no. 4 (1968): 158–163; M. Ullman, S. Krippner and S. Feldstein. "Experimentally-Induced Telepathic Dreams: Two Studies using EEG-REM Monitoring Technique." *International Journal of Neuropsychiatry* 2, no. 5 (1966): 420–437.

14 J. A. Mossbridge, P. Tressoldi, J. Utts, J. A. Ives, D. Radin and W. B. Jonas. "Predicting the Unpredictable: Critical Analysis and Practical Implications of Predictive Anticipatory Activity." *Frontiers in Human Neuroscience* 25, no. 8 (2014): 146. doi:10.3389/fnhum.2014.00146. eCollection 2014. Review.

15 S. T. Wright, C. W. Kerr, N. M. Doroszczuk, S. M. Kuszczak, P. C. Hang and D. L. Luczkiewicz. "The Impact of Dreams of the Deceased on Bereavement: A Survey of Hospice Caregivers." *The American Journal of Hospice & Palliative Medicine* 31, no. 2 (2014): 132–138. doi:10.1177/1049909113479201. Epub 2013 Feb 28.

16 C. W. Kerr, J. Donnelly, S. T. Wright, S. M. Kuszczak, A. Banas, P. Grant and D. L. Luczkiewicz. "End-of-Life Dreams and Visions: A Longitudinal Study of Hospice Patients' Experiences." *The American Journal of Hospice & Palliative Medicine* 32, no. 3 (2015): 269–274. doi:10.1177/1049909113517291. Epub 2014 Jan 16.

17 E.g., J. A. Hobson, C. C. Hong and K. J. Friston. "Virtual Reality and Consciousness Inference in Dreaming." *Frontiers in Psychology* 9, no. 5 (2014): 1133. doi:10.3389/fpsyg.2014.01133. eCollection 2014.

18 E. Aserinsky and N. Kleitman. "Regularly Occurring Periods of Eye Motility, and Concomitant Phenomena, during Sleep." *Science (New York, NY)* 118, no. 3062 (1953): 273–274. See review in P. McNamara. *Neuroscience of Sleep and Dreams*. Cambridge: Cambridge University Press, 2019.

19 N. C. Andreasen, S. Paradiso and D. S. O'Leary. ""Cognitive Dysmetria" as an Integrative Theory of Schizophrenia: A Dysfunction in Corticalsubcortical-Cerebellar Circuitry?" *Schizophr Bulletin* 24, no. 2 (1998): 203–218; F. T. Melges, J. R. Tinklenberg, L. E. Hollister and H. K. Gillespie. "Temporal Disintegration and Depersonalization during Marijuana Intoxication." *Archives of General Psychiatry* 23 (1970): 204–210.

20 P. McNamara. *The Neuroscience of Religious Experience*. New York: Cambridge University Press, 2009.

21 Claude Gottesmann and Irving Gottesman. "The Neurobiological Characteristics of Rapid Eye Movement (REM) Sleep Are Candidate Endophenotypes of Depression, Schizophrenia, Mental Retardation and Dementia." *Progress in Neurobiology* 81, no. 4 (2007): 237–250; J. Allan Hobson. *The Dream Drugstore*. Cambridge: MIT Press, 2001; Rainer Kraehenmann. "Dreams and Psychedelics: Neurophenomenological Comparison and Therapeutic Implications." *Current Neuropharmacology* 15, no. 7 (2017): 1032–1042.

22 Armando D'Agostino and Silvio Scarone. "From Dreams to Psychosis: A European Science Foundation Exploratory Workshop. Editorial." *Consciousness and Cognition* 20, no. 4 (2011): 985–1936; Rainer Kraehenmann. "Dreams and Psychedelics: Neurophenomenological Comparison and Therapeutic Implications." *Current Neuropharmacology* 15, no. 7 (2017): 1032–1042; Patrick McNamara. *Dreams and Visions: How Religious Ideas Emerge in Sleep and Dreams*. Brain, Behavior, and Evolution. Santa Barbara: Praeger, an Imprint of ABC-CLIO, LLC, 2016.

23 Roland Griffiths, Matthew Johnson, William Richards, Brian Richards, Una McCann and Robert Jesse. "Psilocybin Occasioned Mystical-type Experiences: Immediate and Persisting Dose-related Effects." *Psychopharmacology* 218,

no. 4 (2011): 649–665; Roland R. Griffiths, Matthew W. Johnson, William A. Richards, Brian D. Richards, Robert Jesse, Katherine A. MacLean, Frederick S. Barrett, Mary P. Cosimano and Maggie A. Klinedinst. "Psilocybin-Occasioned Mystical-type Experience in Combination with Meditation and Other Spiritual Practices Produces Enduring Positive Changes in Psychological Functioning and in Trait Measures of Prosocial Attitudes and Behaviors." *Journal of Psychopharmacology* 32, no. 1 (2018): 49–69; Roland Griffiths, W. Richards, A. McCann and U. Jesse. "Psilocybin Can Occasion Mystical-type Experiences Having Substantial and Sustained Personal Meaning and Spiritual Significance." *Psychopharmacology* 187, no. 3 (2006): 268–283.

24 Roland R. Griffiths, Matthew W. Johnson, William A. Richards, Brian D. Richards, Robert Jesse, Katherine A. MacLean, Frederick S. Barrett, Mary P. Cosimano and Maggie A Klinedinst. "Psilocybin-Occasioned Mystical-Type Experience in Combination with Meditation and Other Spiritual Practices Produces Enduring Positive Changes in Psychological Functioning and in Trait Measures of Prosocial Attitudes and Behaviors." *Journal of Psychopharmacology* 32, no. 1 (2018): 49–69.

25 David E. Nichols. "Hallucinogens." *Pharmacology and Therapeutics* 101, no. 2 (2004): 131–181; D. E. Presti and Presti, D.E. and Nichols. (2004) Biochemistry and neuropharmacology of psilocybin mushrooms. In: Metzner, R. and Darling, D.C. (eds) Teonanacatl (pp. 89–108). Four Trees: El Verano, CA

26 Rainer Kraehenmann. "Dreams and Psychedelics: Neurophenomenological Comparison and Therapeutic Implications." *Current Neuropharmacology* 15, no. 7 (2017): 1032–1042; Rainer Kraehenmann, Dan Pokorny, Leonie Vollenweider, Katrin Preller, Thomas Pokorny, Erich Seifritz and Franz Vollenweider. "Dreamlike Effects of LSD on Waking Imagery in Humans Depend on Serotonin 2A Receptor Activation." *Psychopharmacology* 234, no. 13 (2017): 2031–2046.

27 Pierre Maquet, Jean-Marie Péters, Joël Aerts, Guy Delfiore, Christian Degueldre, André Luxen and Georges Franck. "Functional Neuroanatomy of Human Rapid-eye-movement Sleep and Dreaming." *Nature* 383, no. 6596 (1996): 163–166.

28 Robin L. Carhart-Harris, Suresh Muthukumaraswamy, Leor Roseman, Mendel Kaelen, Wouter Droog, Kevin Murphy, Enzo Tagliazucchi, Eduardo E. Schenberg, Timothy Nest, Csaba Orban, Robert Leech, Luke T. Williams, Tim M. Williams, Mark Bolstridge, Ben Sessa, John Mcgonigle, Martin I. Sereno, David Nichols, Peter J. Hellyer, Peter Hobden, John Evans, Krish D. Singh, Richard G. Wise, H. Valerie Curran, Amanda Feilding and David J. Nutt. "Neural Correlates of the LSD Experience Revealed by Multimodal Neuroimaging." *Proceedings of the National Academy of Sciences of the United States of America* 113, no. 17 (2016): 4853–4858; Suresh D. Muthukumaraswamy, Robin L. Carhart-Harris, Rosalyn J. Moran, Matthew J. Brookes, Tim M. Williams, David Errtizoe, Ben Sessa, Andreas Papadopoulos, Mark Bolstridge, Krish D. Singh, Amanda Feilding, Karl J. Friston and David J. Nutt. "Broadband Cortical Desynchronization Underlies the Human Psychedelic State." *The Journal of Neuroscience: The Official Journal of the Society for Neuroscience* 33, no. 38 (2013): 15171–15183.

29 Ibid.

30 Petr Bob and Olga Elouchakova. "Dissociative States in Dreams and Brain Chaos: Implications for Creative Awareness." *Frontiers in Psychology* 6 (2015). www.frontiersin.org/article/10.3389/fpsyg.2015.01353, doi:10.3389/fpsyg.2015.01353; Dieter Vaitl, Niels Birbaumer, John Gruzelier, Graham A. Jamieson, Boris Kotchoubey, Andrea Kubler, Dietrich Lehmann, Wolfgang H. R. Miltner, Ulrich Ott, Gebhard Sammer, Inge Strauch, Ute Strehl, Jiri Wackermann and Thomas Weiss. "Psychobiology of Altered States of Consciousness." *Psychological Bulletin* 131, no. 1 (2005): 98–127.

31 I. Limosani, A. D'Agostino, M. L. Manzone and S. Scarone. "The Dreaming Brain/mind, Consciousness and Psychosis." *Consciousness and Cognition* 20, no. 4 (2011): 987–992; L. Palagini and N. Rosenlicht. "Sleep, Dreaming, and Mental Health: A Review of Historical and Neurobiological Perspectives." *Sleep Medicine Reviews* 15, no. 3 (2011): 179–186.

32 Mark W. Mahowald, Michel A. Bornemann and Carlos H. Schenck. "State Dissociation, Human Behavior, and Consciousness." *Current Topics in Medicinal Chemistry* 11, no. 19 (2011): 2392–2402; Dalena Van Der Kloet, Harald Merckelbach, Timo Giesbrecht and Steven Jay Lynn. "Fragmented Sleep, Fragmented Mind: The Role of Sleep in Dissociative Symptoms." *Perspectives on Psychological Science* 7, no. 2 (2012): 159–175.

33 Claude Gottesmann and Irving Gottesman. "The Neurobiological Characteristics of Rapid Eye Movement (REM) Sleep Are Candidate Endophenotypes of Depression, Schizophrenia, Mental Retardation and Dementia." *Progress in Neurobiology* 81, no. 4 (2007): 237–250; Kevin R. Nelson. "Near-death Experience: Arising from the Borderlands of Consciousness in Crisis." *Annals of the New York Academy of Sciences* 13301, no. 1 (2014): 111–119; L. Palagini and N. Rosenlicht. "Sleep, Dreaming, and Mental Health: A Review of Historical and Neurobiological Perspectives." *Sleep Medicine Reviews* 15, no. 3 (2011): 179–186.

34 Denise J. Cai, Sarnoff A. Mednick, Elizabeth M. Harrison, Jennifer C. Kanady and Sara C. Mednick. "REM, Not Incubation, Improves Creativity by Priming Associative Networks." *Proceedings of the National Academy of Sciences of the United States of America* 106, no. 25 (2009): 10130–10134.

35 H. V. White. *Metahistory: The Historical Imagination in Nineteenth-Century Europe*. Baltimore: Johns Hopkins University Press, 1975; H. V. White. *Figural Realism: Studies in the Mimesis Effect*. Baltimore: Johns Hopkins University Press, 1999.

5   Subjectivity and privacy

We now utilize our focus on the agent intellect to illuminate the subjective feeling of what it is like to be a person, to illuminate subjectivity. How is the agent intellect experienced phenomenologically? What does it feel like when we experience the agent intellect in action? It feels private, and there is an inwardness that is not available to, or shielded from others. Most of the time, this inwardness feels like "optimal flow" creativity, imagination, actuality or suchness, centeredness, ecstasis or moving out of the private realm and into others, and the public and power. We experience it most fully when we dream, daydream, imagine, reflect and love. It is the heart of who I am—the center of my Being. It is the image of God within me. The agent intellect is our subjectivity. This chapter attempts to develop a provisional phenomenology of the agent intellect—a description of its experiential qualities. It will build upon Edgar Sheffield Brightman's account of subjectivity discussed in a previous chapter. An accurate phenomenological account of subjectivity will require acknowledgment of an existential realm of privacy where no-one and no-thing, not even God can enter. Only the owner or the person himself can access that interior inwardness. The hope is that an exploration into the phenomenal qualities of this private realm will open up some new ways to think about personalism; the human condition; and the agent intellect, i.e. the metaphysical basis of eschatological personalism. Although God is "nearer to me than I am to myself" (Augustine, Confessions IV), according to eschatological personalism there is nevertheless a part of me that is mine and mine alone. God cannot penetrate that center without the consent of the person. Without that center we would not be autonomous beings. We would not be free. We would not be real. The agent intellect constitutes that immutable center but that name makes it seem cerebral and bloodless. It is time to describe the experience of the personal in more detail.

While it is true that persons are social through and through, their social identities and social relationships do not exhaust who they are. They are still individuals and there is a portion or area within each person that is not penetrated by the social and can never be accessed by any Other at all. Not even God can penetrate to this secret recess as God elects to step back from the individual and his secret interior heart in order to allow the individual ontological room to stand forth in existence as something more than a mere appendage of some other greater being.

But because God withdraws from that inner heart or realm of who I am, at the center of the personal, at the center of who I am, is a God-less "place". But that place is not a hopeless or bereft place because "I" am in it AND some residuum of God is there as well—namely the lingering trace of his invitation to friendship and collaboration. That lingering invitation constitutes the receptive, passive pole of my subjectivity while the consideration/ deliberation/preparation to accept or refuse that invitation constitutes the active pole in my subjectivity. The God-less place at the heart of my being yields despair when I turn my face away from God as it constitutes a temptation to usurp God's role and be the sole creator and ruler of the universe. But when my face is turned toward God there is no despair, as I can consent to let Him in. There is instead anticipation, hope (even before I make the decision to collaborate), and freedom. Thus, the private realm is the source of nothingness, tragedy, and evil in the human experience, but it is also the source of friendship with God. Everything depends on the choice or decision we make concerning God's invitation to friendship. That choice, furthermore, has to be made every moment of my existence.

Religious people and theologians and philosophers of religion like to claim that God is constantly with us or constantly observing or watching us, but that surely is a totalitarian concept of God. Do you really want God to be watching you constantly? Must there be a witness of every moment? There has to be a place wherein the individual can choose if he or she wishes to be alone. This stance or area within the individual has to remain off limits to all others, including God, if the individual is to be considered real, that is, if the individual is to have the ability to stand alone unaided for more than an instant.

Let us call this part of the personal the private realm of the individual. It is central to autarchy and eschatological personalism. The importance of the private realm is not just a practical or legal or human rights issue; it is also a metaphysical issue. To be real is to be self-sustaining and resistant to change for at least some finite period of time. Yet most religious doctrines deny the independence of the individual outright. Buddhism claims that all things undergo co-dependent origination. Everything is empty because every given thing or individual depends on every other thing or individual. The Abrahamic religions define human beings as creatures that are utterly dependent upon God. But God would be a poor creator if all he made were creatures who could not withstand a few seconds without succor from their creator. Like the neo-Platonists of the Roman Empire, some forms of Hinduism see the individual as a mere emanation of the Godhead or the One. While the Daoist and Confucian philosophies of ancient China opened up some room for the reality of the individual, they were interpreted over the centuries in a collectivist manner and tended to see the individual as an appendage of social forces like the ancestors, family, and the state. Thus, the issue of privacy should be a central plank in the battle against oppressive forms of religion, and the development of an eschatological personalism.

Privacy and solitude, furthermore, speak to the ways in which each one of us is different from every other individual. It expresses the haecceity of each individual. It thus inscribes the peculiar identity that each one of us exhibits over the course of a lifetime. The thing that I cannot share with another—the thing that another cannot even see—is my interiority, my subjectivity, my private self. That private realm also cannot be decomposed into smaller parts. If it could, it would mean that the private realm was indeed dependent on some larger whole for its composition. But if we are to account for the existence of individual objects we have to admit that there is something in individuals that allow them some temporary independence of all other things—else individuality would be a meaningless term. For something to be an individual means precisely that it can stand independent and alone for some non-trivial period of time. It cannot be subject to instantiation by any other whole. It cannot be assimilated into any other entity. Eschatological personalism asserts that the mind-body entities that we are will be reconstituted at the resurrection and so will not pass away like all other things. It (the resurrected person) is therefore not something that will pass away. It persists because it is immortal.

Whence comes that ability to resist instantiation? At the level of the personal the element that resists assimilation into larger wholes or reduction into smaller parts is the unity associated with the agent intellect. But we experience the actuality of the agent intellect, initially, as a kind of primary affectivity, consciousness, or primary non-reflective subjectivity. Each person's first-person perspective is a private realm and utterly unique to that individual, and no-one else has access to it. That is why it is private—no-one but the individual himself has access to it. It is what I and others like Brightman have called the "given".

Designation of a private realm inevitably has widely ramifying economic, legal, and political repercussions. The private realm sets limits on the power of the collective or the state to coerce individuals. On the other hand, privacy has all too often been used as an excuse to exclude certain classes of individuals from the public realm and therefore from political power. If, however, the private realm just is what we have been calling the given or the shining present or primary affectivity, then it is a realm of inviolable dignity that is automatically infused with political rights and political voice. Proposals to dispense with private versus public spheres of action and experience need to be careful not to throw the baby out with the bathwater. The personal is the vital wellspring of human interactions. The state and civil society almost inevitably see it as an enemy to be crushed precisely because it cannot be assimilated into these larger wholes. A wise and humane civil society and polity will build in safeguards to protect against incursions into the realm of the personal.

With the modern Western classical liberal tradition, especially its anarchist strain, my reading of the personalist tradition suggests that the modern state and the realm of public affairs in general should be understood to serve the interests of the private realm, and not vice versa. Carving out a private realm in a sense creates the public realm. The public realm is all that is not the private realm. That is why definition of the private realm must be individual and personal, rather than based on group categories. It has been pointed out that attempting to evacuate the private realm of all political content is not viable (and vice versa). Given that the private realm defines what might be considered the public realm, the eschatological perspective I am developing here is roughly consistent with that point of view. While the eschatologically private realm cannot be conflated with the realm of the family, sexuality, private property, and household affairs more generally, it certainly intersects with all of those activities. The mere fact that at the dawn of the modern age most of these activities were assigned to the female while public affairs were assigned to the male suggests that politics cannot be excluded from the private realm and private matters reach into the public realm. Despite, however, the interpenetration of public and private spheres, the eschatologically private realm is strictly personal. Neither the family, the spouse, the partner, the friend, or the colleague can enter into the eschatologically private realm. It is strictly personal. But because it is the one place in the universe where Godlessness prevails it can be a source of evil. It therefore must be intrinsically political and of primary concern for the public and the state. It is the site of a cosmic and supernatural battle between those who want to prevent the coming Kingdom of God from manifesting versus those who want the kingdom to reign. It is therefore through and through political. Without the private realm there would be nothing to fight about and therefore no politics at all. Nevertheless, we cannot collapse the public into the private or vice versa. We avoid both of those errors once again via employment of the *analogia entis* principle. With respect to the divine-human relationship the *analogia entis* principle entails that the human participates in God's divine life but can never match it fully. There is thus a similarity to God but it is strictly limited such that no matter what degree of similarity we attain, there will always be an infinitely larger dissimilarity between us. This "similarity in difference" relationship also obtains when the relationship between the private and public realms is kept in healthy balance. The public realm serves the private just as the human being serves God. The public realm participates in or intersects with the private realm, but it can never capture it or experience it, or reach it fully or penetrate it fully. The public realm can get better and better at understanding, respecting, valuing, and experiencing the sacredness of the private realm, but it will never reach an end to that process. To some extent the healthiness of the public realm depends on its ability to better and better approximate to its appreciation and protection of the private ... but it will never attain to a perfected commonwealth as it will reach the end of that effort to appreciate the private realm. The similarity within an ever greater dis-similarity captures the right sort of balance between man and God and between public and private such that there is no danger of ultimate dissolution of the private into the public. Nor is there the opposite danger of experiencing no connection at all between the two spheres. Instead the connection is real and capable of intensifying to an infinite degree.

The private realm in the current age is eschatological insofar as it embodies or manifests that war between the two temporalities of the current versus the coming age. We all experience that internal war when we experience our wills or ourselves as divided. Akrasia or weakness of will is a symptom of this internal war. Part of me wants to indulge that appetite, wants to eat that chocolate cake, while the other part of me, my future eschatological self, says, "No. If you acquiesce in that appetite you will be harming me by making me fat". That sense of a divided self has its roots in the Godlessness at the center of my subjectivity. Before I consent to the friendship of God there is a moment or pole of experience within my subjectivity that is Godless. That godlessness paradoxically gives me ontological weight as I am momentarily separate from God and a real entity. But it also opens me up to all kinds of potential trouble if I defer decision or refuse friendship with God. So my private realm gives me infinite ontological weight as it constitutes my reality as separate from God and as the site of decision for or against God. It therefore is a prerequisite for my health and freedom. Although it is protected from invasion even by God, it nevertheless can be influenced by the public realm. That is because that phase within my private self that deliberates around the decision to accept God's invitation to friendship can be influenced by presentation of reasons, beliefs, desires, attitudes, and in general by the messages received from the surrounding culture. Its sacred inviolability therefore needs to be protected. Loss of privacy directly leads to loss of the ability to freely deliberate around choices, desires, and attitudes.

Lynch has pointed out that "The connection between loss of privacy and dehumanization is a well-known and ancient fact".[1] Lynch argues that to be an autonomous person is to be capable of having privileged access to information about your psychological profile—your hopes, dreams, beliefs, and fears. To see why Lynch proposes the following thought experiment:

> To get a sense of what I mean, imagine that I could telepathically read all your conscious and unconscious thoughts and feelings — I could know about them in as much detail as you know about them yourself — and further, that you could not, in any way, control my access. You don't, in other words, share your thoughts with me; I take them. The power I would have over you would of course be immense. Not only could you not hide from me, I would know instantly a great amount about how the outside world affects you, what scares you, what makes you act in the ways you do. And that means I could not only know what you think, I could to a large extent control what you do.

Lynch is obviously correct. If someone has total or even partial access to your daily thoughts, fears, and desires, they could control your behaviors by simply manipulating those thoughts, fears, and desires. You would not be free in any meaningful sense. You would be an object for the controller— not an autonomous person.

> From ... the perspective of the knower—your existence as a distinct person would begin to shrink. Our relationship would be so lopsided that there might cease to be, at least to me, anything subjective about you. As I learn what reactions you will have to stimuli, why you do what you do, you will become like any other object to be manipulated. You would be, as we say, dehumanized.

Lynch thus concludes, rightly in my view, that privacy is central to subjectivity, to freedom, to personal autonomy. But as we all know privacy is under relentless attack by the modern national security state which is now equipped with super-intelligent artificially intelligent or AI machines that perform their surveillance activities 24/7.

How do we protect the private realm and promote solitude and contemplation? We can advocate for privacy protections in the public realm but ultimately conscience and privacy or personal choice can only be protected via autarchy wherein the individual learns to govern his own impulses and appetites to such an extent that he cannot be ruled by others or by groups or the surrounding culture. Self-determination and freedom are only possible in conditions where privacy is a real possibility and hopefully protected. Privacy is best protected by virtuous, self-governing individuals. I cannot freely develop my own life plan or follow my own idiosyncratic choices if I cannot control who has access to my bodily person and my mind.[2] As John Stuart Mill argued, my liberty should be given as free a reign as possible as long as it does not harm others.[3] The health of a polity depends on the health of its individuals and the health of the individuals, in turn, depends on respect for their personhoods and personhood, in turn, depends on the private realm or heart of the person which cannot be assimilated into any other whole without destroying it. This classical liberal conception of the private self expressed in the language of "rights", along with neglect of the language of responsibility, of course, carries with it tremendous potential cultural problems as it lead to all kinds of atomistic and individualistic greed, crime, and social anomie. Nevertheless, we need to preserve its core insight on the inviolability of the individual conscience and heart.

First we must know what is the private innermost self? The unified conscious experience, the first-person perspective, the agent intellect is the heart of subjectivity and autonomy. The "heart" is the focal point or the center of gravity of the affective life. It is incommensurable with any other thing or person as it is utterly unique to the individual because it embodies the particular response each individual enacts to the given and to values.

It is not the "secrets" each individual hides from the world. Nor is it the secret desires the heart entertains. Nor is it some homuncular self or little inner child that memory attempts to protect from the outside world. All of these things gain their charge from their connection to the *still point* but they are not the still point.

The *still point* is the agent intellect; it reflects the unique thisness, haecceity, or special perspectival experience of the individual upon awakening to the gift of existence/being that is primary subjectivity. Our first response to the gift of subjectivity and life is one of simple awareness of the "suchness" of things, of life, and a feeling of awe and wonder. This simple, calm awareness can be accessed anytime via meditation and contemplation, but only by individuals. It occurs only to individuals. Because access becomes difficult over time as the initial reception of the gift is forgotten or if it later gets buried under layers of other responses, special effort is needed to learn, paradoxically, how to give up all effort and relax back into that primordial gift of compassionate, calm, awareness of what is.

This is not some speculative claim on my part. The fact that this state of calm, unified awareness exists has been experimentally verified literally thousands of times by thousands of practicing Buddhist, Hindu, and Christian contemplatives across the centuries, and now more recently in the laboratory. We even know what brain activation patterns accompany this state. The recent large number of studies on mindfulness meditation experimentally confirms that (1) the state exists, (2) the state can be accessed by anyone after proper training, and (3) the state is associated with beneficial effects on psychological and physical health.[4]

Mindfulness is described as the awareness that emerges by engaging in the act of non-judgmental noticing of experiences as they unfold in the present moment.[5,6,7,8] There is strong experimental evidence derived from gold-standard double-blind randomized placebo-controlled trials that mindfulness meditation alleviates stress and improves symptoms of myriad physical and psychiatric disorders. Multiple functional imaging studies of brain activation patterns associated with mindfulness suggest that the most consistently activated regions are those involved associated with daydreaming, namely the default mode network (DMN). The DMN is activated when people just daydream or let their minds wander. The medial prefrontal region, the anterior cingulate, the posterior cingulate, cortical midline structures, the insula, the amygdala, and some basal ganglia structures are the sites most often activated during mindfulness mediation.[9,10,11,12,13] These are also the main sites involved in the DMN.

Thus, the unified first-person awareness that is at the heart of subjectivity and of privacy is not some construct made up by philosophers—it is documented and verified by experiment and by the functional magnetic resonance imaging or fMRI of the modern laboratory.

Subjectivity

What then is subjectivity? It is the heart of the person. It is one pre-reflective experiential pole of the agent intellect. Subjectivity is not what happens when I self-reflect. My subjectivity is not what happens when I take myself as an object of my thought. Subjectivity is not a special instance of intentionality or object consciousness. While I can self-reflect I need not do so in order to experience my subjectivity. Instead my subjectivity, as many of the phenomenologists have pointed out, is immediately given to me and I experience it spontaneously. I am *it* spontaneously. I need not do anything but be, and I am immediately immersed in subjectivity. It is the experience of sheer actuality that is the agent intellect. The heart of the person, eschatologically speaking, is the sea of images, affects, and qualia that present to me as possibles. They reflect my freedom as they literally are the forward part of the sea of possibilities that are my future. I am immersed in my subjectivity whenever I sit back, relax, and daydream.

When we place a subject in a magnetic resonance imaging scanner and have them do nothing in particular we see a consistent set of activations in the DMN—that set of functionally inter-connected regions including medial prefrontal, inferior parietal, medial temporal, posterior cingulate, and the ventral precuneus. The brain is quite active even when no effort at self-reflection or directed thought is involved. Note that all these regions are known to involve very high-level integrative information processing functions. The subject reports feelings, images, mind-wandering, anticipatory hopes and worries, bodily feelings, and all kinds of fantasies. This is the kind of subjectivity that we all experience as spontaneously given to us whenever we sit still and do nothing in particular. Note that some aspects of this so-called "default mode network" have been identified even in infants and it is clearly identified in children as young as 7–9 years old.

The French philosopher Michel Henry suggested that subjectivity is nothing less than, or nothing more than the manifestation of life in the individual.[14] It is experienced as affectivity, an oscillatory passing from suffering to joy and back again. It is a *passio* or passion, something undergone, a spontaneous reception of an upsurge of life, a gift and a feeling, not something accomplished or cognized. It is immediate given-ness. It is immanent interiority, not transcendental intentionality toward an object out there at some distance from myself. Rather my subjectivity is immediately given as self-affectivity and passion. It is a non-intentional revelation of the self for the self. Before any act of transcendence or intentionality, before directing my thoughts or affects toward some object in the world, being—my being appears as spontaneous affectivity and radical interiority.

Henry is surely correct to break with the standard view that subjectivity arises in relation to an external object or an external other. There is a subjectivity that exists prior to any encounter with an other, whether that other is an object or a person. Not every experience requires a subject to own it or an object to give it its content. Experiences of subjectivity seem to come "pre-packaged" as it were with a kind of indestructible unity and given-ness/awareness. Note, however, that self-affectivity, unity, and given-ness, nevertheless, still constitute a form of subjectivity and first-person perspective. It is merely different from the kind of subjectivity that is characterized as intentionality. Directed thought or intentionality is the other pole of subjectivity within the agent intellect.[15]

Henry's view that we are first passive, receptive beings and only later active, agentic beings runs counter to much of modern philosophy and theology. We are not ecstatic beings first. As several Taoist philosophers in the East have argued, we are first manifested as spontaneity, as passive receivers of the gift of life which upsurges in us regardless of whether objects or others are present. Theologically speaking we are called from out of the sea of ideas/possibilities in the Mind of God and freely given existence or Being and partnership/friendship with God. We are free to accept or reject the gift. We are that gift. When God creates a human being, he creates an agent intellect. We fundamentally are the agent intellect in its oscillatory activity between the receptive and the intentional modes. But the gift is first experienced by us as subjectivity and life. When we accept the gift of existence the agent intellect experiences this as primary subjectivity. That initial yes to existence is manifested as primary receptivity but it is followed up by a yes to collaboration with God and then the experience is activity/agency.

That invitation to collaboration however is what is most problematic for us it seems. Fear of friendship with God and the desire for God-like knowledge of good and evil or autonomous creativity create in man a flight from awareness of the gift. The flight from the awareness of ourselves as passive or spontaneous receivers of the "gift" of life leads to all kinds of extreme positions in philosophy, theology, and politics. When we do not root ourselves in our true subjectivity as spontaneity, we over-emphasize the transcendent and ecstatic aspects of our being. We become too cerebral and spiritual, deny the body, and condemn earthly existence as nothing but evil and suffering. When on the other hand we get stuck in the receptive form of subjectivity, that of passive reception of the gift, we tend to forget our obligations to be active in partnership with God and to work for the relief of suffering and the pursuit of justice for others. In previous chapters I have discussed Aquinas's and Pryzawrara's *analogia entis* as a potential solution to the dilemma of over-emphasizing immanence or transcendence. Although we carry an element of the divine within and are therefore somewhat similar to God (transcendent pole) we are nevertheless far more dissimilar to God (immanent pole) than we are similar. As Eric Voegelin[16] has emphasized, the proper vocation for man is the in-between state or *metaxy*—not too high and not too low, not too transcendent, and not too immanent. That is the still point at the heart of man, where life seems to carry you along just where you need to go.

The overwhelming tendency of philosophers in the West however has been to fly from the immanent and to model subjectivity as activity rather than spontaneity. That there is some sort of activity within the affectivity that is given to me as spontaneity however cannot be denied. In fact, "activity" appears to be just as much a given experience or phenomenon as spontaneity. The spontaneous experiences we undergo have import for the embodied being or individual and therefore must be to some extent intelligible. First-person perspective is obviously associated with the fact that we are embodied beings who can feel pain and joy, who are attracted to value and attempt to move away from dis-value. If experiences had no significance for the individual there would be no selective noticing or valuing of one experience over another and therefore no first-person perspective.

Brightman's "shining present" can spontaneously register a "beyond itself", even though its primary manifestation is pure given-ness or immanence. Brightman's other pole in his analysis of subjectivity is called the "illuminating absent". It is part of the structure of our spontaneity and our affectivity such that some element of reference beyond the immediate exists or occurs. It does not concern the "past" only. Detachment from the immediate present is also accomplished via reference to a future. Thus, the given may be experienced as anticipation of change or affect currently being undergone, or it may be experienced as an awareness that the stream of experiences I am currently undergoing is partially differentiated and is passing away. Qualia are not all the same. They constitute a plurality and to the extent that they constitute a plurality some are similar in structure or related to one another while others seem utterly unrelated to others. Some are identical to the different affects that I undergo but others are not, so their sources may differ as well. Identification of plural experiences may also suggest that there are other "shining presents" or agent intellects out there that seem to respond to my signals and vice versa. They are part of my stream of consciousness right from the start. They are part of the given.

All of these considerations point to the clear fact that in immediate given-ness we can also discern structural differences in "properties" or qualities of experiences and as soon as these differences are admitted the issue of reference arises because differing experiences must be related in differing ways to differing experiences and therefore patterns emerge. To discern difference is to discern potential patterns and this sort of discernment suggests a guiding agent intelligence that exhibits preference for some experiences over others and so on. Once discernment occurs as part of the immediately given experience we undergo (and as argued above, this discernment MUST occur if we are embodied beings), then reference beyond the shining present and toward the illuminating absent (both past and future) is inevitable.

Discernment and preferences bring with them the beginnings of first-person perspective and the possibility that there is patterned information in the experiences we undergo. If patterned information is present then intelligibility is worth cultivating rather than mere awareness of experiences.

The self that manifests first-person perspective and some amount of pattern seeking behavior is the "minimal" self, or the "basic" or "core" self or its "ipseity". This is still a *prereflective,* or tacit level of selfhood. Only minimal agency is involved and consists in the mere act of discernment or preference of some affects over others as well as some minimal anticipatory states of good or bad things to come. When however we add to preference an active selection process, then it is reasonable to believe that the agent intellect's key activity of actualizing some possibles over others is operative. Here some experiences are rejected while others are appropriated or actualized. When those experiences are both actualized/preferred and appropriated, they become "my" experiences, though we have not yet described how this appropriation process occurs. It may be that the appropriation process is simply the end result of the actualization process. Once a possible becomes actual it is automatically appropriated as mine. Actualization involves the addition of qualities to an idea or form. That is an intentional process. When no new qualities are added the thing is actualized.

Appropriation of preferred experiences can only occur if there is an entity that is set apart from the rest of the experiential universe and that is endowed with or has the capacity to prefer some experiences over the others and then to inhibit, deflect, or reject the non-preferred experiences while allowing the preferred experiences to presence/remain/actualize. The idea is that we are immersed in a sea of possibilities all waiting to be actualized. We do so via a selection process involving inhibiting all other possibilities until we are left with the intended target. Then we add new qualities to that target and it is ipso facto actualized when no new qualities are added. Ownership, in short, boils down to the ability to push away or reject or to not grasp non-preferred experiences. It is the ability to let some experiences fall away from some stable position. Does ownership then merely require the ability to withhold the tendency to grasp some experiences to keep them from falling away? Probably not, as an entity is required that has some content or set of experiences that it has grasped and held against loss for some period of time. Persistence across time of same content is required before we can speak of some stable entity that is capable of appropriating preferred experiences over non-preferred experiences, i.e. ownership. But to create that stable entity appropriation has to occur and the ability to hang onto preferred experiences and to resist destabilization for some period of time has to occur.

How do experiences resist change over time? If we assume that change is real, and I think we must if we are to account for novelty and creativity, then things change at different rates. Some change more quickly than others and stability may merely indicate a slower rate of change for things that "resist change". We cannot assume that everything changes at the same rate or that change is instantaneous or immediate. If all things changed at the same rate we would not be able to detect change at all because we would not be able to take up a stand from which to measure change. And if things

changed instantaneously there would similarly be no way we could measure change because as soon as we tried to do so change would again occur.
So the things we experience must change at a rate that allows us to notice
varying rates of change.

So how do stable entities form against constant change? If we assume
that the agent intellect is an immortal entity then the problem of persistence
is solved. But even if we set that assumption aside for argument's sake, persistence can still be achieved. We have seen that first there is the immediate
"shining present" that comes equipped with some unity of awareness of
current affectivity. That must mean that this shining present resists change
in its experiential makeup simply by changing at a slower rate than other
centers of experience. We have also noted that a discernment or reactive
process also occurs as a kind of illuminating absent and that this illuminating absent indicates some ability to refer to, or register something beyond
its own immediate state or its own rhythm of change and to the extent
that that is possible some amount of discernment or preference also occurs.
At first preference may be merely for other experiences with similar rates
of change and then as time goes on preference evolves into preference for
sameness of content or similar or complementary experiences and so on.

Whitehead and the process metaphysicians have also suggested another
route to stability or persistence in their concept of "prehension" meant to
describe perception. Here a current center of experience or "actual entities"
or "occasions" or the given in Henry's sense is assumed to be influenced by
a past set of experiences in an asymmetric dependence relation. The present is influenced by the past but not vice versa. The present integrates past
experiences to create novel actualities which have as their "illuminating
absents" the past experiences they just integrated or prehended. The past
experiences also to some extent cause the present set and thus causality is
brought into the picture. The whole process by which the past is integrated
into present experience is cumulative, so growth is inherent in the process.
Thus stability or substance is analyzable into a special kind of relation: that
of prehension or the succession of states of experience into actual entities
via prehension.

Whether stability of a center of experience is due to a process like prehension or due to a chance slowing down of the rate of change in a set of
experiences relative to other centers of experience or to some other unknown process entirely, some amount of stability is required for ownership
to emerge. I suggest that ownership, the feeling that these are MY experiences and not those of some other center of experience, emerges from the
discernment or selection or preferences for some experiences or possibilities
over others. We are immersed in a sea of possibilities but our subjectivity,
the gift of the given, allows us to consistently prefer some types of these
possibilities over others and that leads to stability of content. If we are in
partnership with God we will prefer those possibilities that best manifest
the transcendentals. But if we are not in partnership with God, we will

prefer those possibilities that appear to create power we can use, i.e. those possibilities that mobilize force for domination of Nature and others.

The integration of experiences (whether via prehension of some other process) likely involves some optimization process such that the integration process aims at harmony or resonance among present elements; those that fit are integrated and those that do not fit are ignored or rejected. Harmonization, preference, fit, or selection raises the absolutely essential issue of valuation in the experience of given-ness, ownership, agency, and the minimal self. The transcendentals represent for eschatological personalism the highest criteria for "fit". Normative religious and spiritual values likely also operate to guide fit. For a center of experience or an actual entity to persist across time it has to retain some experiences and discard others and this "decision" process implies a valuation process. Valuation is part of the immediately given experience. The immediately given is not just a passion or an undergoing of affectivity as Henry argued. It is also a valuation process and this too is gift; it is immediately given to consciousness to choose among an array of experiences using the transcendentals as a criterion of fit or selection. The immediately given subject who undergoes suffering and joy also has to choose among experiences that he or she or it wants to integrate into current consciousness. Choice implies a minimal amount of agency and therefore we see that the immediately given awareness of the actual entity comes equipped with both a passive, experiential (patient) pole of experience and with the beginnings of an active agentive valuation pole such that subjectivity has to be construed in an apparently dipolar manner that combines a moment of pure experience with a moment of active choice or agency. The agent intellect unites both poles of experience.

We can express the same facts discussed above in terms of tri-polar relation as well. While I experience much in myself as spontaneously given feelings and ideas, these affects and thoughts are constantly in flux and changing. They cannot form a basis for stability or persistence. As soon as I notice that change in my spontaneous affects, feelings, images, and ideas, however, I also notice that the change is sometimes non-random. Some affects/images/ideas change in relation to other contents of my spontaneous awareness. When certain images come to mind the affect I experience changes non-randomly. Some are associated with joy, others with need, and still others with anticipation and so forth. Life upsurging in me can be an upsurging of excitement and desire, an anticipation of possibilities and things to come or a foreclosing of possibilities given the limitations of my body and context. These brute facts of my embodiment and existence introduce a second moment in my subjectivity that is different from spontaneity—a moment rooted in my spontaneity but different from spontaneous affect. I would experience no anticipations without the upsurging of life in me so things like anticipatory affects are rooted in spontaneity. Yet they are clearly different from spontaneous affect as they point to potential ends of affects. My spontaneity is logically prior to my anticipatory affects as I could not experience the latter without the former, yet they are both my immediately given subjectivity. The second moment affects/images/ ideas tend to be responses to first moment affects/images/ideas. Second moment affects/images/ideas co-inhere with the original spontaneity and are a reaction to its spontaneous feelings and aversions rooted in my existential situation as an embodied human being living in this time and place. They tend to be reactive desires, fears, anticipations, and mental simulations or images of anticipatory states of affairs. But again even though the second moment logically depends on the first moment they are both my immediately given subjectivity. Self-reflection in the sense of taking my subjectivity as an object of thought has not yet entered the picture. We are still at the level of the immediately given. To complete the picture of the immediately given we have to note that after spontaneity of affect generates anticipatory simulations and desires there is a process that mediates between and unifies spontaneity and simulation. The first and second moments interact and communicate with one another such that the anticipatory simulation is experienced as a spontaneous and involuntary affect that issues in a unified erotic and ecstatic experience of desire. It is this erotic synthesis of affect and anticipatory simulation that leads to ecstatic opening to an other that is an oft noted aspect of subjectivity. This opening toward an other is a third moment that occurs in subjectivity. It constitutes the appropriation or "ownership" process wherein some affects/images/desires are "owned", stabilized, selected while others are allowed to fall away. That this third moment of subjectivity involving synthesis is also a moment of appropriation and ownership is confirmed by the fact that the opening toward the other cannot be indiscriminate. The spontaneously given anticipatory states are oriented toward simulated states of fulfillment or values that "speak to" or match its needs and desires. To the extent that the anticipatory states or desires are firmly rooted in the moment of spontaneity the resultant ecstatic synthesis of spontaneity and desire will issue in an orientation toward the future and the infinite as spontaneity itself is a manifestation of the infinite energies that manifest as an upsurge of life in subjectivity. Conversely the opening toward an other is also an orientation toward the future and the infinite given that desire and love intend the future and can never be exhausted.

At the heart of the subjective therefore is a synthesis of an inward looking *abyssal infinite* manifesting as spontaneity and an outward looking *ascending infinite* manifesting as eros. The inward looking abyssal infinite constitutes one of the sources of ablative love, such as agape. The outward looking ascending infinite manifesting as eros is one of the sources for erotic desire, love, and devotional forms of religion. The synthesis between the two movements toward the infinite constitutes the origins of love that constitutes the "heart" of the individual. The heart is that place within the individual that is most truly the individual. It is the center or core of the person. It is the still point at the center of the person. As T. S. Eliot famously wrote:

> At the still point of the turning world. Neither flesh nor fleshless;
> Neither from nor towards; at the still point, there the dance is,
> But neither arrest nor movement. And do not call it fixity,
> Where past and future are gathered. Neither movement from nor towards,
> Neither ascent nor decline. Except for the point, the still point,
> There would be no dance, and there is only the dance.[17]

Readers familiar with Charles Saunders Peirce's fundamental categories of Firstness, Secondness, and Thirdness[18] will note some similarities between Pierce's categories and the phenomenology of subjectivity as outlined here. I believe that the similarities are real and are there but they are not simple identities. In Peirce's scheme Firstness is described as spontaneity, immediacy of experience, ever novel, free, present, whole, and without unity and parts. Secondness depends on Firstness and is composed of hard realities that butt up against spontaneous qualia and experiences. Secondness is composed of facts, relations, results, and what is Other to spontaneous experience. Thirdness mediates between Firstness and Secondness and brings them into a unity, a whole, and a relationship. As mentioned above, the source of the unity of subjectivity is that third moment wherein spontaneity and reactions to spontaneous affects such as anticipatory desire are synthesized in the outward looking ascending infinite or erotic (filiative) desire that is subjectivity as we experience it from the first-person perspective.

From a theological point of view the constitution of subjectivity in terms of Peirce's triadic categories might be seen as exemplifying the Christian claim that man is made in the image of God where God is here understood as the Trinity. Subjectivity is given and is experienced theologically as gift. The recipient is invited to do two things: fully receive the gift and then respond to the gift. Reception of the gift is handled by the synthesizing activity of the Third moment when the inward looking abyssal infinite assimilates and transfers the ever novel upsurge of affects and life energies into the hands of the second moment consisting of reactive anticipatory desires and then feeds these into the outward looking ascending infinite of erotic desire. Response to the gift does not occur within subjectivity. Response to the gift occurs at the level of the whole person with the heart and the agent intellect mediating the whole process. Because God's gift is gratuitous, God does not require or expect gratitude, or any kind of response from the recipient, from subjectivity. That "No response required" gesture from God is another source of inwardness in subjectivity and therefore another source of solitude and the right to privacy. God's gesture of "no response required" places a kind of existential and inviolable space around subjectivity that rests within a kind of joyful inward receptive mode. God does not compel subjectivity into ecstasy or into agentic responding. The sources of agentic responding come from within subjectivity itself as it gives rise to personhood and are utterly free. It is a response out of the freedom of the whole person in relation to the invitation of God to friendship with God.

Notes

1 Lynch, Michael P. "Privacy and the Threat to the Self." *The New York Times*, 2013.
2 See Rossler, Beate. *The Value of Privacy.* Polity, 2005.
3 Mill, John Stuart. *On Liberty.* Longmans, Green, Reader, and Dyer, 1869.
4 Marchand, William R. "Neural Mechanisms of Mindfulness and Meditation: Evidence from Neuroimaging Studies." *World Journal of Radiology* 6.7 (2014): 471.
5 Grossman, Paul, et al. "Mindfulness-based Stress Reduction and Health Benefits: A Meta-Analysis." *Journal of Psychosomatic Research* 57.1 (2004): 35–43.
6 Kabat-Zinn, Jon. "Mindfulness-based Interventions in Context: Past, Present, and Future." *Clinical Psychology: Science and Practice* 10.2 (2003): 144–156.
7 Lutz, Antoine, et al. "Attention Regulation and Monitoring in Meditation." *Trends in Cognitive Sciences* 12.4 (2008): 163–169.
8 Malinowski, Peter. "Neural Mechanisms of Attentional Control in Mindfulness Meditation." *Frontiers in Neuroscience* 7 (2013): 8.
9 Taylor, Véronique A., et al. "Impact of Meditation Training on the Default Mode Network during a Restful State." *Social Cognitive and Affective Neuroscience* 8 (2012): 4–14.
10 Lutz, Jacqueline, et al. "Mindfulness and Emotion Regulation—An fMRI Study." *Social Cognitive and Affective Neuroscience* 9.6 (2014): 776–785.
11 Raichle, Marcus E., et al. "A Default Mode of Brain Function." *Proceedings of the National Academy of Sciences* 98.2 (2001): 676–682.
12 McKiernan, Kristen A., et al. "Interrupting the "Stream of Consciousness": An fMRI Investigation." *Neuroimage* 29.4 (2006): 1185–1191.
13 Northoff, Georg, et al. "Self-Referential Processing in Our Brain—A Meta-Analysis of Imaging Studies on the Self." *Neuroimage* 31.1 (2006): 440–457.
14 Henry, M. *The Essence of Manifestation* (Girard Etzkorn, trans.). The Hague: Nijhoff, 1973.
15 Although it is commonly believed that first-person perspective disappears under anesthesia and deep sleep that may in fact be mistaken. Take the case of deep sleep. Advocates of the belief that first-person perspective disappears under conditions of deep sleep presumably are referring to slow wave sleep as that other form of deep sleep known as REM is now known to be associated with widespread brain activation and often vivid dreams. Slow wave sleep is also associated with widespread brain activation patterns including regionally specific increases in activity in relation to slow waves (brainstem, cerebellum, ventral prefrontal cortex, and posterior cingulate cortex/precuneus, parahippocampus areas). In addition, people can sleep walk and move about avoiding objects when sleep walking all during slow wave sleep. Children can experience "night terrors" during slow wave sleep where they hallucinate some monster and scream bloody terror. Nor is first-person perspective eliminated entirely under anesthesia. General anesthesia is characterized by domination of slow waves characteristic of slow wave sleep throughout selected brain regions. When emerging from general anesthesia people progress gradually from

a pattern characterized by strong peaks of delta (0.5–4 Hz) and alpha/spindle (8–14 Hz) power ('Slow-Wave Anesthesia') to a state marked by low delta-spindle power ("Non Slow-Wave Anesthesia") before awakening. Even during deepest anesthesia approximately two patients per thousand maintain a level of awareness such that they can recall accurately what happened to them during surgery. All patients under general anesthesia can process high-level semantic materials. Associative learning can occur under anesthesia and it is known to involve medial prefrontal cortical networks. Indeed functional connectivity between prefrontal and precuneus regions is enhanced under general sedation. Given that activation of the precuneus is known to be associated with enhanced sense of self and subjectivity increased precuneus functional connectivity under propofol sedation may reflect disconnected endogenous mentation or dreaming that continues at a reduced level during sedation. The prime candidates for functional networks of the forebrain that play a critical role in maintaining the state of consciousness are those based on the posterior parietal-cingulate-precuneus region and the nonspecific thalamus. All of this is not to deny that first-person perspective is not disrupted during general anesthesia. It is only to suggest that first-person perspective is not utterly extinguished in general anesthesia. Anesthetic loss of consciousness is not a block of corticofugal information transfer, but a disruption of higher-order cortical information integration. Therefore subjectivity is not lost during anesthesia—just disrupted.

16 For a good overview of the political philosophy of Eric Voegelin see Franz, Michael. *Eric Voegelin and the Politics of Spiritual Revolt: The Roots of Modern Ideology*. Baton Rouge: Louisiana State University Press, 1992.

17 Eliot, T.S. *Four Quartets*. New York: Harcourt, 1941.

18 *The Essential Peirce*, 2 vols. Edited by Nathan Houser, Christian Kloesel, and the Peirce Edition Project. Bloomington: Indiana University Press, 1992, 1998.

6 Eschatological ethics and the Kingdom of God

Eschatology is the study of last things—the ultimate end, the consummation, and final fulfillment of all things during and at the end of history. With the exception of Berdyaev, previous personalist philosophers did not emphasize the need for an eschatological personalism. For some scientific accounts of the cosmos, all things will end in a deep freeze and a vast meaningless nothingness. But for the world's Abrahamic religious traditions the end involves an apocalyptical judgment and destruction of the evils of this world, a total re-making or re-creation of this world, and then the fulfillment of each individual's personal destiny. The destiny given to each individual is a free gift from God. Destiny and purpose are intrinsic to the eschatological conception of persons because people are created by God to be free, meaning-seeking individuals who live in community with other free creative individuals.

Although not invested in Berdyaev's eschatological vision, virtually all previous personalist philosophers were centrally concerned with building up a political community of free and equal persons. Within the Christian context that community would partially constitute the Kingdom of God. Thus personalist ethics should be concerned with building up the beloved community. Previous personalists developed their philosophies during the 20th-century period of mass political movements and the rise of totalitarian dictatorships around the world. The 20th-century personalists opposed totalitarian regimes of both the right and left. They opposed narcissistic and acquisitive forms of individualism, but also opposed dissolving the self into any ensemble of social relations as that would amount to enslavement and assimilation of the individual into the group or state. Broadly speaking most personalists recommended some version of a pluralistic, liberal, and democratic political order with the principle of subsidiarity guiding legislative decisions: whatever community needs could be fulfilled at the local level should be fulfilled at local level. The aim was to avoid building up the centralizing power of the executive by empowering and building up local, mid-size community organizations that nurtured individual creativity and that were made legally and politically responsive to local people's needs and desires. This ethical and political emphasis on the building up of equitable and just communities of persons needs also to be a part of any eschatological personalism. But the eschatological personalist understands that only God can bring in the Kingdom of God. Our portion is to do what little we can to minimize violence and to build up the beloved community via concrete corporal acts of mercy, participating in the Christian church and cultivating local, mid-size communities and organizations that protect vulnerable persons and the individual. What eschatological personalism adds to this traditional picture of political engagement is the radical relativizing of any current political order (including liberal democratic regimes) in favor of the visionary order that is to come with the Parousia. We give due reverence, loyalty, and obedience to the current order, but we invest in, strive for, love, and hope for the coming order. What kind of order will that be? What are the dangers of emphasizing the visionary preference over the current reality? To answer the latter question we need to first answer the former question.

We cannot specify in great detail what the coming order will look like beyond a few general principles that virtually anyone would endorse. Anyone can proclaim that they are for free, just, and flourishing political communities that protect individual rights, including the rights of the vulnerable, needy, and poor. What eschatological personalism can add to the vague hopes for a just political order is the radical relativization of the current order and some analysis of the dangers and opportunities involved in pursuit of utopian political projects of both the right and the left. In addition, it provides some theoretical grounding around the possibility and means of protection from seduction of malign political forces, the dangers of depersonalizing technology, and an analysis of the sources of humanity's ideas concerning political order.

Political scientists have largely neglected investigation of a major source of political ideas and projects: namely religious communities and traditions. In the global North, and in the "West", both leftist progressive political philosophies/projects and conservative right-wing political philosophies/projects are arguably rooted in old or even ancient Christian theological controversies and movements. Religious ideas, in turn, ultimately come out of religious ideologies and myths, which, in turn, are often rooted in dreams and visions.

How might an eschatological personalist community or movement respond to the current crises facing us all in the 21st century? We will use Wilson's[1] social science typologies concerning political stances religious movements have taken in the past vis-à-vis the larger community to understand our options today. One possibility is that we should attempt to persuade others that our point of view is reasonable (conversionist), i.e. we should aim at changing the beliefs and desires of the regnant surrounding culture. Discussion and dialog, of course, are virtually always beneficial so there is little to be said against this possibility. Sometimes, however, the other side does not want discussion. Instead they want utter submission. In those cases dialog is impossible and the smaller community must consider other options. A second possibility is that we should aim at changing the social structures of the larger community. Instead of attempts at dialog, we should aim at changing the entire social system into something more favorable to our views (revolutionist). This possibility, however, is fraught with dangers and only rarely do better institutions emerge from the fires of a revolution. Adopting a piecemeal approach to changing the surrounding culture and system (reformist) is another alternative. Piecemeal reform is more than just a possibility; it is an obligation of any decent person to attempt to better things, so this is something that applies to all communities. If you or your community however is in imminent danger of annihilation, then you won't be so willing to wait decades or centuries for change. Another option is to forego any attempts at changing the larger surrounding community and instead focus inwardly and withdraw from the world like the ancient Essenes apparently did (introspectionist/introversionist). That way the smaller community can concentrate on digging deeply into their own traditions, solidify them, and prepare for future events. The problem with this stance of course is that the outside world rarely leaves you alone. Yet another possibility is that "we", the smaller community, not withdraw from the world but instead become proficient and expert at something the world needs and thus we acquire power and wealth in the world that could be used to protect and grow our community. In other words, we acquire special knowledge in order to overcome the world (manipulationist). Many minority communities down through the ages have followed this route successfully for varying periods of time but they usually, over time, become part of the world. They become corrupt. The danger is that success in the world usually leads to seduction by the world rather than overcoming the world.

The ancient stoics appear to have decided that all of the above strategies were not applicable to them or did not work for them. They decided that the only possible response to the surrounding corruption of the age they were living in was to withdraw from it and cultivate one's inner freedom. That inner freedom was manifested vividly in the capacity to consent or to withhold one's consent and to never give in. In this way they could protect themselves from social contagion and evil (thaumaturgical). But this individualist "thaumaturgical" strategy applies to every human being and human group. Dignity itself requires that you hold yourself aloof from the surrounding corruption and that you withhold your consent from the evils you are required to witness. While this strategy allows a minority movement or community to survive, it does not help it grow or win. The final strategy is the utopian strategy involving a complete human change of social structures. We do not aim at changing merely beliefs and desires, or merely social structures. We aim at fundamental change. We understand that the aim is utopian but aiming at anything less undermines everything else. Paradoxically, utopianism is the most practical and the most necessary of all political strategies in a corrupted age. You cannot be an effective reformer unless you have a utopian aim and vision. You cannot cultivate your own community traditions unless you have an ideal, a utopian ideal, that will allow you to evaluate the extent to which you depart from the ideal. You cannot protect yourself and your loved ones from the surrounding corruption unless you carry within a utopian vision of how things ought to be.

Where do we get that all-important inner vision of how things ought to be? Eschatological personalism asserts that we each carry within us an intuition of the ideal social form or community. We each have an intense pre-conscious internal dream-like vision of the "beloved community" where conflict, crime, injustice, and pain are eliminated and love is real. That internal intuition of the ideal community, in turn, informs the political goals we all strive for, and it manifests as the continuing efforts to find utopia and build the ideal community. In that ideal community what ought to be is. Consistent with the idea of an *inaugurated eschaton*, the Kingdom of God began with the ministry of Jesus. Its key elements remain alive and growing within the worldwide church, and it will be fully realized with the final and ultimate inbreaking of God into history at the end of the world or the "second coming".

Christian personalism refers to that ideal community as the Kingdom of God. The Kingdom of God, when it comes, will be unprecedented in human history. According to the *Book of Revelation*, the Kingdom will take the form of a New Jerusalem:

> I saw the holy city, the new Jerusalem, coming down out of heaven from God, prepared as a bride adorned for her husband. And I heard a loud voice from the throne saying, "See, the home of God is among mortals. He will dwell with them; they will be his peoples, and God himself will be with them; he will wipe every tear from their eyes. Death will be no more; mourning and crying and pain will be no more, for the first things have passed away."
>
> (Rev. 21:2–4)

This dream-like vision of the Kingdom of God realized on Earth is found throughout the New Testament writings. Right at the beginning of his earthly ministry Jesus proclaimed: Mark 1:14–15 "The time is fulfilled, and the kingdom of God is at hand; repent, and believe in the good news". But what is the Kingdom of God going to be like? It is going to grow organically within the old temporal order, and then the old order will suddenly be cut down: (NRSV) Mark 4:26–29.

> The kingdom of God is as if someone would scatter seed on the ground, and would sleep and rise night and day, and the seed would sprout and grow, he does not know how. The earth produces of itself, first the stalk, then the head, then the full grain in the head. But when the grain is ripe, at once he goes in with his sickle, because the harvest has come.
>
> (NRSV)

It is going to be almost impossible to get into the Kingdom as the door is narrow and few can make it through: Luke 13:22–30 He said to them,

> Strive to enter through the narrow door; for many are called but few are chosen. …Mark 10:23–25 But Jesus said to them again, "Children, how hard it is to enter the kingdom of God! You have to be born of water and the spirit to get into the Kingdom: John 3:3–5 Jesus answered him, "Very truly, I tell you, no one can see the kingdom of God without being born from above".

Nicodemus said to him, "How can anyone be born after having grown old? Can one enter a second time into the mother's womb and be born?" Jesus answered, "Very truly, I tell you, no one can enter the kingdom of God without being born of water and Spirit". In addition, you have to take the Kingdom by force: Matt 11:12 From the days of John the Baptist until now the kingdom of heaven has suffered violence, and the violent take it by force. And yet paradoxically the Kingdom of God is already among us: Luke 17:20–21 Once Jesus was asked by the Pharisees when the Kingdom of God was coming, and he answered, "The kingdom of God is not coming with things that can be observed; nor will they say, 'Look, here it is!' or 'There it is!' For, in fact, the kingdom of God is among you".

For the Kingdom of God is Rom. 14:13 "…righteousness and peace and joy in the Holy Spirit".

And it will involve the resurrected body-mind-spirit of the personality Cor. 15:20–28

> …for as all die in Adam, so all will be made alive in Christ. But each in his own order: Christ the first fruits, then at his coming those who belong to Christ. Then comes the end, when he hands over the kingdom to God the Father, after he has destroyed every ruler and every authority and power. For he must reign until he has put all his enemies under his feet. The last enemy to be destroyed is death.
>
> (1Cor. 15:50–53)

> What I am saying, brothers and sisters, is this: flesh and blood cannot inherit the kingdom of God, nor does the perishable inherit the imperishable. Listen, I will tell you a mystery! We will not all die, but we will all be changed in a moment, in the twinkling of an eye, at the last trumpet. For the trumpet will sound, and the dead will be raised imperishable, and we will be changed. For this perishable body must put on imperishability, and this mortal body must put on immortality.

The Kingdom of God breaks into history in the ministry of Jesus, and the future of the world in this kingdom is made possible because of Jesus's resurrection from the dead thereby defeating death itself. Jesus's resurrection proleptically prefigures the destiny of each individual born of water and spirit in Christ. Jesus has inaugurated the future that awaits for each one of us.

The Kingdom of God as summarized above and adumbrated in the pages of the New Testament constitutes, for eschatological personalism, the *social imaginary* that animates its social ethics and political orientation. The Kingdom of God is experienced as a dream-like intuition of the ideal commonwealth, but it is experienced as uncannily tangible and real in moments of ritual practice, prayer, and meditation. It suffuses all of eschatological personalism's world outlook. It is what we strive to realize and it is what we celebrate as coming to be within and without us in the present moment. So each present moment is oriented toward the future when the fullness of the Kingdom will be realized. Thus, eschatological personalism's emphasis on visionary, dream-like cognitions goes hand in hand with simultaneous cultivation of future-oriented philosophy and thought.

But what are the dangers of anchoring one's political and social hopes in a future age where all will be "righteousness and peace and joy in the Holy Spirit"? The immediate result is that every current political order is relativized. It may well have a legitimate claim of limited obedience and loyalty from the eschatological personalist, but it cannot claim its full loyalty and obedience. Anything that impedes the coming age of righteousness and peace and joy in the Holy Spirit will not be able to claim full obedience and loyalty from the eschatological personalist. Since righteousness and peace and joy are things every sane person desires, both the personalist and the regular partisan of any given political order will claim that his political ideal is best. So, clearly the strengths and the dangers derived from the eschatological orientation come down to how one interprets things, like righteousness, peace, and joy in the Holy Spirit. One man's righteousness is another man's terror, persecution, and blood-letting.

Relativizing every current political order is a chronic destabilizing force for every society that harbors eschatological personalists, but that likely is a good thing. A slightly destabilized society avoids stagnation and is nudged to grow constantly in order to overcome the destabilizing force. This destabilizing tendency derived from the eschatological attitude has arguably spawned the entire liberal progressive tradition that has sought to ever more closely approximate an ideal society via steady expansion of the rights of the individual. The problem, however, is that ever expanding rights of the individual put the entire populace at war with one another as the rights of person/group X tend to interfere with the rights of person/group Y. The state is called in to adjudicate the war of all against all and thus the state grows in power. The progressive tradition in short has failed to limit state power. Thus, the progressive response to the destabilizing element in the eschatological element in Christian society cannot work in the long run as it requires totalitarian state controls at some point in its evolution. Another negative effect of valorizing the future utopian ideal over the current order is that that valorization can be used as justification for the most egregious acts of inhumanity and violence against opponents of that ideal. If you think all goodness and light is on your side, then opponents can only be criminal and satanic. Thus, any means, no matter how violent, can be used against them. This all too familiar justification of violence and murder is a lamentable constant of utopian political movements, but it can be controlled and eliminated from utopian political rhetoric and practice.

Immanentization of the eschaton (utopianism) is a danger, but so is its opposite: investing the immanent, the current political order, with all value. From this point of view what exists is what is to be valued. Believing that the good is always anywhere else but where you are is a self-defeating de-lusory stance. Accept the Now, say the partisans of the current age. Invest *what is* with all value. It is, after all, all that we will ever have. Root your stand in reality—not in some delusory hopes about the future. You can attempt to improve what we have, but don't devalue it as nothing compared to what could be! The partisans of the "present moment" certainly seem to make a lot of sense—except for one inconvenient fact: the Now quite often is horrifying. Suffering, misery, injustice, and horror are all too real parts of the Now. Attempts to improve the Now, when they are not utopian, are like mere bandaids on festering, life-threatening open sores. Even if the NOW were not filled with suffering and misery, you cannot really ap-preciate the NOW without some standard by which to appreciate it. That standard can only come from a hierarchy of values. In the case of political forms the standard comes from comparing what is with what ought to be, i.e. a utopian ideal.

In summary, attempting to immanentize the eschaton or eschatologize the immanent is unworkable. The correct balance between the two poles can be struck by privileging the future utopian ideal, but not totally devalu-ing the present, and then interpreting the utopian ideal in humane, person-alist terms. The political principle should follow the metaphysical principle of *analogia entis*: similarity of Being within a greater dis-similarity such that the more similar one becomes to God the greater the dis-similarity will manifest. Man occurs in the balance between two extremes. He is not God (transcendent) but he is not purely animal either (immanent). He contains an image of the divine and participates in the transcendent but does not leave his earthiness behind. In political orders there should be an element of the transcendent within the immanent, i.e. there should be some similarity between the two poles. But the immanent does not get swallowed up by the transcendent or vice versa. There is similarity between the immanent and the transcendent but greater dis-similarity. The immanent can never fully reach the transcendent and the transcendent can never be collapsed within the immanent.

Advances in technology tend to destabilize the political order as well and in several ways. One way not often commented upon is that the evolution of machine technologies tends to upset the balance between the immanent and the transcendent poles of the political order. Nudged by tech visionaries and their oppositional counterpart Luddites, most people tend to see tech advances as weighting the balance in favor of the transcendent sphere. Each new tech innovation is used as further evidence to argue that human beings are achieving God-like control over the Earth and its riches. Other tech innovations make it possible for some human beings to wipe out whole cities and nations. It is no wonder that advances in technology promote a kind of forgetting of human limitations and an over-estimation of the divine element in human being. When the transcendent pole becomes the sole focus of a population, hubris and then madness are not far to follow. Whom the gods would destroy they first make mad.

Technology is the wild card when it comes to political order. While the eschatological element in political forms tends to slightly destabilize the order, rapid advances in technology significantly destabilize things. There have been many political responses to destabilizing technologies. The Luddite response of choosing to halt technological change rarely works and even when it does work you give up whatever benefits that technology would have brought.

The accelerationists of both the right and the left argue that the only way through the technologically supported post-capitalist neoliberal world regime is to help the system collapse under its own weight.[2] Capitalism infused with super-intelligent, artificially intelligence (AI) is a system that cannot be defeated in the usual ways. With the creation of super-intelligent machines the system itself may have finally fashioned the thing that will bring the system crashing down once and for all. In particular, if super-intelligent machines begin to see the human species as impossible to deal with given the differences in intelligence and speed of thought, the machines may decide they no longer have use for the human species. Then the machines will simply ignore our needs or outright eliminate us. If the accelerationists want to drain the system to its dregs and let it crash and burn under its own contradictions, what do we do about the super-intelligent machines? Once they become aware or once they reach a certain level of intelligence we may be so dependent on them that we could not pull the plug on them without harming ourselves. Accelerationism does not appear to have a rational program for dealing with these possibilities.

What then is the solution? There is no one solution. Turning our lives over to the machines, however, will surely change what it means to be a person. Even if the machines do not pose an existential threat to the very survival of humanity, greater dependence on these machines will surely dramatically change what it means to be human. One prudent step would be to slow down any processes that make us too dependent on the machines. We need to become less vulnerable to the promises machines make to us.

Autarchy as the fundamental stance of an eschatological personalism

Another possible ethical response to the rise of intelligent machines as well as the axial age we are living through is to get one's own house in order, to cultivate one's own virtues. We will be better able to resist seduction of the machines of tyrannical regimes if we are less enslaved to our own appetites. Self-government sounds pretentious and complicated but it is really very simple. Self-control over one's desires, impulses, and goals confers a modest amount of immunity to attempts by others to control your desires, impulses, and goals. Being able to resist one's impulses and to prioritize goals helps you (but does not guarantee of course) to resist destructive appeals from others. Autarchy or self-rule follows logically from the fact that persons are essentially free beings. Because they are metaphysically and ethically ultimate they cannot be constrained, coerced, harmed, or assimilated into any group. They own and rule themselves. Now, of course, persons are daily and routinely constrained, coerced, harmed, and assimilated. But my claim is that despite all of these evils routinely inflicted upon persons, the freedom inherent in personhood, the ability to consent and to bring selected possible worlds into actuality remains inviolate. The person can only be implicated in those evils if he or she consents to them, i.e. if he or she voluntarily gives up self-rule. As prisoners everywhere have always known one can remain free even in prison. Conversely, one can be a slave even if one is not in prison and one employs slaves. Freedom is a spiritual fact and is active as long as life is in the person. The essence of freedom is the capacity to call into being (from the realm of possibilities) things that conform to the true, the good, and the beautiful. Slavery is the refusal to do so. Collaboration with God is necessary if one is to call things into being that manifest the true, the good, and the beautiful so freedom manifests when one collaborates with God and is lost or compromised when one turns away from that collaboration.

Autarchy has obvious affinities with anarchism, libertarianism, and Junger's Anarch. It agrees with anarchism's suspicions about the state, but also knows that the state can protect us from chaos and chronic disorder. The state can also sometimes protect the weak and vulnerable. Autarchy agrees with libertarianism that we should avoid whenever possible increasing powers of the state and that most decisions should be made at local levels obeying the principle of subsidiarity. But autarchy is incompatible with the possessive, acquisitive individualism endorsed by most libertarians.

Self-rule if it means anything means self-control and the cultivation of the ability to delay immediate gratification of impulses in order to obtain future rewards. Autarchy implies the revival and valorization of asceticism and ritual practices that increase self-control. Eschatological personalism can meet the challenge of the rise of intelligent machines and the related consolidation of totalitarian powers of the modern technocratic state because it protects individuals from all forms of enslavement that emanate from these sources. Take for example the account of the negative effects of technology provided by Heidegger and Junger. When we bring into being knowledge related to technology that act has the side effect of placing us into an existential stance of what Heidegger called "standing reserve". That is the production of knowledge concerning power and control over nature and others via technology has the secondary effect of subordinating human beings to that power. Every time we create a new machine, we simultaneously gain additional control over Nature and others, but that includes us, the creators of that technology. As Junger argued technology has the tendency to promote the total mobilization of forces in a society and then the use of that force against Nature and against persons. In short, technology can enslave its users and creators just as much as it can dominate Nature and enemies. To prevent the kind of relationship to machines that entails human enslavement, eschatological personalism short circuits the "standing reserve" and similar coercive effects of technology. Eschatological personalism asserts that bringing any knowledge into being should be guided by the transcendentals of truth, beauty, and goodness. When those transcendentals guide the actualization of possibilities and the production of knowledge that knowledge ensures the flourishing of human beings rather than their enslavement. In addition, it prevents any kind of master-slave relationship between persons or between machines and persons or between persons and Nature. It prevents any person from being treated instrumentally because it asserts that persons are ultimates, end-in-themselves with infinite dignity. In addition, if a person roots his identity in what we subjectively experience as the future, then that person's spiritual capacities will embody all of the knowledge available to persons in that future when the Kingdom of God has come and thus transcend any machine whose knowledge capacities are limited by the present. In short, the fact that eschatological persons will be guided by the transcendentals means that their preferences in knowledge and in everything else (theoretically at least) will be for anything that strengthens that free activity and self-rule. Autarchy is fundamental to eschatological personalism and thus slavery to others or to machines is inimical to eschatological personalism. That, of course, does not mean that eschatological persons will be stronger or smarter than others or than super-intelligent machines. It simply means that eschatological persons will be a bit more *immune to seduction* by super-intelligent machines and thus eschatological persons will have a bit more elbow room to maneuver against the machines if necessary. The autarch will be free from absolute need and dependence on super-intelligent machines. Although the emotional distance that eschatological persons will have from super-intelligent machines will admittedly be miniscule, it will be a trait few other persons will have in the coming age and it will make all the difference in the war to prevent domination of the human race by those machines. That resistance to servility or assimilation into any power, entity, group, or process that curtails one's freedom comes directly from the eschatological focus on self-government or autarchy.

Autarchy or the ability to support individuals that can delay gratification of impulses is fundamental to creating a working society. The ability to delay gratification can be indirectly studied by looking at factors that influence temporal discounting. The rate at which individuals discount the future relative to the present based on the opportunity cost of delay is exponential apparently indicating that people reduce/discount the value of a reward if there is a delay in getting the reward. Even when there is an opportunity to obtain a larger reward there is still a preference for smaller immediate rewards over larger ones in the future. Discounting rates vary considerably across individuals but there appears to be an inherent tendency of people to undervalue future rewards and events. Nevertheless, future orientation and the ability to value some future rewards as much as immediate rewards are associated with a host of benefits for the individual and society. Without the ability to build up a future orientation or an ideal future self we are vulnerable to control by current stimuli and current impulses. The paradigmatic case of control by current self or current impulses is addiction. The addict is locked in the present and assigns all costs of the addiction to the future self. For the addict, the future ideal self is nebulous in the extreme compared to the screaming demands of the current craving self. There is no ideal future self that can inhibit, modulate, suppress, and control those cravings. The current self becomes imperious and tyrannical. Future consequences are discounted in exchange for an immediate pleasurable experience. One way to build up the future self is to develop precommitment mechanisms that kick in when the cravings start to control the current self. The individual sets up consequences that take effect immediately whenever cravings intrude. In this case the current self stops dumping the costs of acting on cravings onto the future self. So the future self can come out from under the thankless task of cleaning up after the current self's binges. A more traditional way to build up the future self is to engage in religious and ascetical practices. Akrasia is a Greek term that roughly means weakness of will power. It literally means "lack of self-mastery", the opposite of autarchy. Akrasia occurs when the current self overpowers the future self as in addiction. The relation is asymmetric. The future self never swallows up the current self. The closer the current self is to the future self the stronger the will power is. This observation is consistent with the eschatological idea that the real self is anchored in the future eschaton.

In terms of personal future-oriented thinking we are always attempting to become an ideal version of ourselves. We want to be a better person, a richer person, a more famous or honored person, a better-looking person, a more beloved person, a slimmer person, and so on. The desire to be someone "better" is a huge motivational factor in a person's behavior and ultimately his sense of self. I am not a mere day laborer—I am a writer who is not yet published. I am not a penniless musician—I am a future rock star and so on. Although it is easy to mock our fantasies of future glory, these future selves can make us better persons. The closer a person identifies with his or her ideal hoped-for future Self, the more likely it is that that person will be able to delay immediate gratification in order to obtain larger future rewards (like saving for retirement), saving for a rainy day, practice exercise and healthy eating habits, and start and finish an educational program of study. For these people their identities are literally rooted in their future selves. It is the future self that determines their behaviors, choices, and day to day lives.

Whether we like it or not this is the case for all of us—even if we fail miserably to live up to our future ideal hoped-for self. That future self still exerts a regulatory and motivational effect on our lives. We all identify ourselves with what we believe we are to become. If our idea of our future self is healthy or ideal then we tend to fare better in life. If on the other hand we see no rosy future for ourselves then we will not fare so well. Psychologists have studied these remarkable relationships between current versus future selves in terms of the construct of "possible selves". Possible selves are the selves we hope to become and the selves we fear becoming. Both hoped-for and feared selves are motivating. We strive to become the hoped-for self (successful and healthy), and we strive to avoid becoming the feared self (jobless and sick). The striving for a hoped-for self and avoiding a feared self facilitate activation of approach/avoidance systems. In this way, possible selves function as cognitive and emotional motivators toward some future goal-directed behavior, and serve as self-regulatory processes.

An ideal possible self can be cued by social context and often is cued in religious contexts. If the surrounding culture is reinforcing things like planning for long-term goals then hoped-for selves are more likely to be triggered and accessed. If, on the other hand, the surrounding culture is reinforcing hedonistic immediate gratification of impulses, then the distance between ideal and current selves is likely to be large with all of the personal distress that that incurs.

Culture both interacts with and is influenced by every individual's pursuit of and identification with their personal ideal future selves. To the extent that identification with an ideal future self is supported by the culture, that culture tends to be healthy. By healthy I mean that it is economically prosperous; its citizens have savings. They plan for the future. They build cities and communities for the future. They invest in education and learning. Crime is low and few experience poverty. The pursuit of an ideal future self is also intertwined with an individual's "reproductive strategy". If you feel no identification with a hoped-for future self you tend to adopt a short-term opportunistic orientation toward mating and parenting in which sexual intercourse with multiple partners occurs earlier and romantic relationships are short-term and unstable. This orientation is geared toward increasing the quantity of offspring as early as possible. If on the other hand you feel a strong identification with a hoped-for ideal future self then you are more likely to adopt a long-term investing orientation in which sexual intercourse occurs later in life with fewer partners, pair bonds are long-term and more stable, and personal investment is greater. This orientation is associated with delayed maturity and with maximizing the quality of offspring via intensive investment in each child.

What are the cultural cues that generate adoption of a long-term reproductive strategy associated with the hoped-for future self? One possibility is that when mortality rates are high in an area, the optimal reproductive strategy will be to eschew hoped-for ideal selves and instead start sexual activity early and maximize current fertility rates despite the chaotic local environment. When, however, local mortality rates are low, hoped-for ideal selves seem more possible and the best strategy would involve deferred long-term reproduction in which fewer offspring are given better and more long-term care. But persistent, cross-generation high mortality rates are rare in human history. If they were persistent we would be extinct as a species. So what other cultural cues occur that can generate investment in hoped-for ideal selves? Some authors have suggested the presence of grandparents, particularly grand-fathers, would be an excellent piece of evidence that disease and war have not occurred locally for some time and therefore may not occur imminently. Therefore adoption of a long-term reproductive strategy would be reasonable and generation of hoped-for selves would be supported.

To return to how possible selves motivate behavior: once a possible self is cued by the surrounding culture and imaginally generated by the individual, it needs to become motivationally salient before it can exert an effect on self-regulation. That is, there needs to be a felt difference between the current self and the possible self for any possible self to motivate any kind of behavioral adjustments. Next, the possible self must seem to be achievable or preventable for the person involved. Here again the surrounding cultural environment is crucial. In tribal societies ceremonial and ritual initiation rites would support individual's pursuit of ideal future selves. In modern societies access to educational opportunities likely supports similar goals. To make education accessible a society needs investment capital but to attain investment capital its citizens need to avoid debt and accumulate savings. To accumulate savings citizens need to adopt a belief in a future hoped-for ideal self so it is clear that culture and individual constitute a feedback loop where each requires the other to flourish. Attaining to a possible self is more likely if there are specific strategies developed to attain or avoid that self. Those strategies are discovered via ritual ceremonies, educational events, and via peer interactions. Most importantly we can better identify hoped-for selves if we have models or heroes that embody the kind of person we want to become. The possible self is more attainable if it is linked with these kinds of heroic models or at least important social identities. And finally, the current self has to feel that the amount of effort expended to achieve this self must be congruent with the felt importance of the possible self.

This story concerning the ways in which we generate and pursue our intentions, free activity, and ideal future selves makes it clear that it is a process of accessing imagined possibilities, desires, and goals and then making some of those possibilities a reality via the hierarchical implementation of various intentional states. Goal pursuit, particularly of ideal selves, exemplifies the process of free activity as it chooses among free possibilities to make some of those possibilities actual. This free activity of the person reflects, manifests, shows, or gives us indirect proof that unity in consciousness makes committed long-term goal pursuit possible. After all, if there were no unity in consciousness intentional states would not be generated consistently. One intentional state could contradict another randomly. Implementation of or realization of intentional states would fluctuate randomly. Goal pursuit processes in the brain allow us to see unity in consciousness at work as it supports all ongoing activity streams so as to accomplish aims and goals. The aim or end-state imparts the content or unity to the organism. Unity/haecceity is accomplished/manifested/unveiled via the realization of or movement toward the end state. Although the above considerations make it clear that we experience our true selves as rooted in future hoped-for ideal selves (since that is what we work for on a daily basis) it does not exhaust the ways in which the human brain is really concerned with the future.

There has been a remarkable coalescence of work from both the theological and scientific communities on the significance of future-oriented thinking for human experience. This work on future-oriented thinking can deepen our understanding of persons and help to build up communities of free persons. Szpunar et al. (2014)[3] distinguished among four modes of future thinking including *simulation* or surveying or imagining possibilities for the future, *prediction* or modeling possible futures, *intention* or focusing on a possible future, and *planning* or preparing for that possible future. We can see these four modes of future-oriented thinking as a description of the process of bringing possibilities into progressively more concrete actuality. When we realize or bring to life a possibility, we first canvas or search an array of possibilities in our imaginations; we then select a subset of that array and test this subset via use of predictive models of how those possibilities might play out in real life; we then select the best of the test models and embed these models into an intention to actualize them; and finally, we prepare to implement or actualize those possibilities.

People spend more time thinking about the future than the past. While future orientation can sometimes increase worry and anxiety, it can also act as a buffer against feelings of hopelessness and depressive symptoms. Future orientation has also been found to be related to higher levels of academic achievement, improved economic decision-making, higher levels of well-being, self-acceptance, personal growth, and autonomy and greater economic security. Future orientation also tends to promote greater investment in savings and when large numbers of people build up their savings accounts there is a greater pool of investment capital available that entre-preneurs can use to launch companies thereby improving economic condi-tions in the country. Preis et al. (2012)[4] found that the future orientation of a country was positively related to the gross domestic product of a country. You begin with individuals increasing their abilities to delay gratification of impulses. These abilities both enhance and are enhanced by future orien-tation. Future orientation then leads to savings for the future and planning for the future. When millions of people develop this future orientation you have a shot at a flourishing community. Autarchy is not a mere individualist position within personalist philosophy. It is the precondition for commu-nity. The better able we are to become our ideal future selves the more the eschatological personalist ideal will be realized.

Evnine[5] recently argued that to be a conscious person one had to assume certain knowledge structures aimed at the future. Conscious persons are agents; agents necessarily involve/require deliberation; and deliberation re-quires belief states, including second-order belief states (I believe that he believes that...). Second-order beliefs also entail beliefs about one's own beliefs or reflection about one's own beliefs. Evnine argued that we should add a new criterion for rational personhood, namely that persons should, in the absence of contrary evidence, treat their future beliefs/selves as their current beliefs/selves. Up to some limit in old age beliefs tend to improve over time so persons should adopt those beliefs.

The classical Boston personalists worked out a consistent system of eth-ics that can be read as the set of virtues required to build up a future ori-entation or a future self. The original personalists were primarily social ethicists and theologians. They therefore were quite concerned to argue that ethics and personality were intimately connected and were founda-tional for building up the beloved community. The ultimate value was, in fact, personality and all other values followed from that primary commit-ment. But the ethical implications of that ultimate value were embodied in Brightman et al.'s system of ethics described below. The "Principle of the most inclusive end" referred to the injunction to form and aim at a coherent life project to guide one's choices and behaviors. The "Principle of the ideal of personality" referred explicitly to making the ideal future self a norma-tive goal for one's ethical choices.

Ethical value for consciousness is what the medieval scholastics called the true, the good, and the beautiful and what the classical tradition called the good life. Just as in the Chinese Confucian tradition so too in the Greek and Roman classical tradition: the eudemonistic pursuit of the good life involved avoiding extremes, aiming for the still point at the center of one's experiences. The cultivation and practice of the virtues were recommended, with prudence and wisdom guiding the daily practice of the virtues. The personalists argued that one could not gain access to the good life and the ability to appreciate the true, the good, and the beautiful except through the modality of the personal. Personality is the prime good.

What ultimate values follow from the primary value inherent in the personal? Bertocci and Millard (1965)[6] built upon Brightman's system of ethics but in addition attempted an explication as to how individuals gradually become the ideal future self they were meant to be (see Table 6.1).

Brightman, Bertocci, and Millard explicated a system of moral principles that began with the injunction to be rational and logically consistent in your choice of moral principles and ended with the injunction to choose the ideal of personality as an ultimate moral principle. We add one eschatological principle that is consistent with all the other principles in Brightman et al.'s system: we ought to guide all our acts by the ideal conception of what the whole personality (our own personality and Others) will become at the Eschaton. The Eschaton is a regulative ideal that is only dimly perceived from within this life. 1 Corinthians 13:12 King James Version (KJV) *For now we see through a glass, darkly; but then face to face: now I know in part; but then shall I know even as also I am known.* If we see and remember that our highest possible ideal self will finally be manifest at the Eschaton then we should act as if that is the core of who we are NOW. The highest ideal possible Self is the fulfillment of the particular idiosyncratic destiny assigned to each individual by God. A person who has manifested all that God has intended him to be will no longer be imprisoned in Time. All mind and brain functions given over to temporal frames of reference will fall away. He will live in community with Others and with God. He will live face to face with God in friendship and collaboration.

Each of the successive moral principles built upon the preceding principles such that the whole set constituted a rationally coherent and mutually supporting system of personalist ethical principles. For example, the third principle in the series, the axiological principle, says that "All persons ought to choose values that are consistent with each other, harmonious, and coherent, not values that are conflicting, contradictory or incoherent". This third principle obviously builds on the first two principles—the principle of logical consistency and the principle of autonomy. These first two principles are formal as they depend on the formation of right intentions. To choose morally I need to form the intention to do so and that implies the right use of reason and rationality. The principles I choose as moral laws to guide my actions need to pass the test of rationality and they need to be freely chosen by me. I need to choose them without coercion as rationality requires choice based on reasons rather than coercion. But once I choose freely and rationally I need further to choose higher moral values rather than immoral values. This is what a rational free being would and should do. I call upon my reason to do so. I notice that it is in the nature of things that values come in hierarchies. Rationally I ought to choose my set of values such that they are a harmonious set—otherwise they could not guide me in everyday decision-making. If the values I chose conflicted with one another no rational action would be possible and any moral project I had would be defeated.

Similarly, the principle of specification builds upon the preceding five principles—the two formal principles and the several axiological principles.

The principle of specification is in my view one of the most important of moral laws formulated by the personalist (besides, of course, the last eschatological principle and the most inclusive ideal of the personal itself). The principle of specification states that "Each person, in any given situation, ought to develop the value specifically relevant to that situation". So, if two values can be realized in a situation choose the one most relevant and context specific. This principle of specification is extremely important because it is the one that guides us in the heat of everyday life when all kinds of conflicting values contend for our attention and favor. How do I choose from amongst the range of choices I am faced with each day in a thousand different situations? The principle states that I choose the value that the situation itself is most in need of. The context gives us the clue as to what value to realize in order to satisfy the previous principles in the series (logical consistency, autonomy, axiological harmony, consideration of consequences, and aiming for the best possible outcome) and the final personal ideal itself. Both the principle of specification and all the preceding ones in the series that make the principle of specification possible give us the criterion upon which to choose to make the concrete situation realize the highest values possible within the limitations of the specific context itself.

Let us see how the principle of specification might work in practice. Sartre (1957)[7] described a student who wanted to join the French resistance against the Nazi occupation. His brother had been killed in the German invasion of 1940. But the student's mother did not want her only remaining son to leave and risk death in the resistance. She needed him there. What should the student do? The principle of specification suggests that the immediate moral context is the distress his mother will feel if he leaves to go fight the enemy. Staying to comfort his mother, furthermore, does not violate the first five principles. For example, logical consistency is protected because it is reasonable to assume that a higher value (protection of the mother) is satisfied by the decision. Autonomy is respected as the decision is made without coercion. The principle of best possible is satisfied given the context and the principle of specification is also satisfied given that comforting a distressed mother is the highest relevant value available to choose in that immediate context. Comforting the mother is also consistent with the overall ideal of respecting the personal, with the idea of altruism and the principle of ideal control.

So what about his duty to his country? Staying to comfort his mother would violate the injunction to do all he could to build up the beloved community, unless comforting his mother could be considered building up community. Leaving his mother to fight in the resistance furthermore is consistent with logical consistency and autonomy as the decision is made without coercion. The principle of respecting the personal and the idea of altruism are consistent with leaving the mother and fighting in the resistance. But the principles of specification and ideal control are not met (given that his brothers were killed in the war and that combat is unpredictable). Overall, fewer ethical principles are satisfied with the scenario of leaving the mother; therefore, the student should stay with his mother.

Ethical commitments are fundamental to personality. Personality can profitably be understood as realized via a mental and affective commitment of the individual to what is construed by that individual as "ultimate" in value. My personhood, as the personalists have argued, represents the cumulative effect of my commitments to values over the course of a lifetime. I become what I value. The first obligation is to become my ideal self. Then I will be better able to love others and to help realize the beloved community.

Table 6.1 Personalist ethics

I. *The Formal Laws*	
Logical principle	Each person ought to choose values and behaviors consistently or logically. Reasons for actions should be intelligible and guided by the transcendentals
Principle of autonomy	All persons ought to recognize themselves as obligated to choose in accordance with ideals that they acknowledge.
II. *Axiological Laws*	
Axiological principle	All persons ought to choose values that are consistent with each other, harmonious, and coherent, not values that are conflicting, contradictory, or incoherent. This principle implies that I do not choose values that would interfere with implementation of ideals and values higher in the hierarchy.
Principle of consequences	Each person ought to consider and approve of the foreseeable consequences of his actions. The individual should take responsibility for his actions insofar as consequences are foreseeable.
Principle of the best possible	Each person ought to choose the best possible values in every situation and hence, if possible, improve every situation. This is the personalist complement to the physician's "First, Do no harm". Prudence guides everyday application of virtues.
Principle of specification	Each person, in any given situation, ought to develop the value specifically relevant to that situation. If two values can be realized in a situation choose the one most relevant and context specific.
Principle of the most inclusive end	Each person ought to choose a coherent life in which the widest possible range of values is realized in accordance with a life plan. Each person ought to develop a life project and use consciousness to reflect on his whole life project.
Principle of ideal control	All persons ought to control their empirical values by their ideal values. Self-realization and realization of the life plan ought to be consistent with one's highest ideal.

III. Personalistic Laws	
Principle of individualism	Each person ought to realize in his own experience the maximum values of which he is capable in harmony with all other moral principles.
Principle of altruism	Each person ought to respect all other persons as ends in themselves and as far as possible cooperate with others in the production and enjoyment of shared values.
Principle of the ideal of personality	We ought to guide all our acts by the ideal conception of what the whole personality ought to become both individually and socially.
Principle of community	Each person ought to do his utmost to realize the beloved community.
Eschatological principle (addition by McNamara 2019)	We ought to guide all our acts by the ideal conception of what the whole personality (our own personality and Others) will become at the Eschaton.

Notes

1 Bryan R. Wilson, *Religion in Sociological Perspective* (Oxford: Oxford University Press, 1982); *The Social Dimensions of Sectarianism: Sects and New Religious Movements in Contemporary Society* (Oxford: Clarendon Press, 1990).

2 For a compendium of accelerationist thought see the papers in #Accelerate# edited by R. Mackay and A. Avanessian, Urbanomic Media LTD, Falmouth, UK, 2017.

3 K. K. Szpunar, R. N. Spreng, and D. L. Schacter. A Taxonomy of Prospection: Introducing an Organizational Framework for Future-Oriented Cognition. *Proceedings of the National Academy of Sciences of the United States of America* 111, no. 52 (2014): 18414–18421.

4 Tobias Preis, Helen Susannah Moat, H. Eugene Stanley, and Steven R. Bishop. Quantifying the Advantage of Looking Forward. *Scientific Reports* 2, Article number: 350 (2012): 1–2. doi:10.1038/srep00350 L3.

5 S.J. Evnine. *Epistemic Dimensions of Personhood* (Oxford: Oxford University Press, 2008).

6 P. Bertocci and R. Millard. *Personality and the Good: Psychological and Ethical Perspectives* (New York: David McKay Company, 1967).

7 Jean-Paul Sartre. "Existentialism Is a Humanism," Trans. Philip Mairet, in Walter Kaufmann (ed.), *Existentialism from Dostoevsky to Sartre* (New York: Meridian, 1957/1946), 287–311.

7 The divided self
Groups, evil and depersonalization

The personalist project sets the person at the center of the moral universe. What is inimical to the person or destructive to the person is potentially evil. Ultimately what is destructive to the person is the refusal of the invitation of friendship with God or collaboration with God. When we fail to collaborate with God in our efforts to bring things out of the realm of possibility and into the realm of the actual, the things we bring into being are often monstrous or inimical to the well-being of persons. There is a distortion or privation of the process by which the individual agent intellect brings intelligible forms into being. When the effort involves interactions with other persons there is a failure to grasp the value inherent in the self or other person. The cause of the failure may be many things, perhaps the agent intellect prematurely terminates the transfer of what the medieval scholastics called intelligible forms out of the realm of the possible or potential existence and into the real and actual. Or it could be due to a failure to use the transcendentals to guide the actualization process. Or more frequently it could be due to a failure to grasp the unique value of the person you are interacting with. In this chapter I look at what an eschatological personalism can tell us about certain forms of evil. To forecast the key conclusions: some forms of evil, especially those related to group-inspired depersonalization of self and others, must be considered more than just privation of Being. All forms of evil act to delay the Parousia—the coming age.

Evil and the agent intellect

According to Aquinas the agent intellect operates only on universals but according to Scotus and others the agent intellect can also grasp the haecceity or uniqueness of an individual or a particular. To see and grasp the value of an individual requires an appreciation of the uniqueness of that individual. Normal person perception begins with grasping universals concerning the person such that he or she is placed into preexisting categories of race, gender, socioeconomic class, and so forth. If the cognitional/actualization process stopped there no new qualities or values concerning the person are discovered; instead simple determinations concerning the person are computed so as to categorize the person due to race, sex, etc. After categorization is accomplished the cognitional process can then proceed along one of two lines: if it wishes to grasp the individuality, the haecceity of the person, the cognitional process will engage in further processing of information about the person to discover what makes him/her different and unique. That discovery process involves additional grasping of accidentals or qualities of the person. Discovery of the uniqueness of the individual inhibits treatment of the individual as less than valuable because it grasps and brings into being the unique values associated with that person. While uniqueness itself is a value, persons are also valuable in whatever ways they have exemplified the transcendentals in their lives. To grasp the moral uniqueness of the individual you need to let yourself be guided by the true, the beautiful, and the good in your estimations of that person's essence. If you are not guided by the transcendentals in your cognitions about the other person then by default you let yourself be guided by local cultural or group norms in your estimations of other persons. Now most of the time this is necessary and harmless as we will not interact with the other person nor have any power over that other person. But when personal interactions are called for and if we have power over that other person then we should be guided by the transcendentals as much as possible when considering that person. This rule is nothing more than a restatement of the golden rule.

If, however, the cognitional process does NOT take the route to grasp the haecceity of the person and instead lets itself be guided by group bias, it is in danger of treating the individual as a means rather than as an end and dehumanizing the individual. That distortion is ultimately tied to a poorly guided interaction between freedom of the will (rooted in Love) and the deliberative process of the agent intellect which refuses to let the transcendentals guide the cognitional process and follow the route toward grasping the uniqueness of the individual of interest. I now want to make the argument that that poorly guided interaction between will and intellect in the agent is, in turn, rooted in group bias.

Group bias

Group bias refers to the fact that most human groups necessarily operate to further group interests regardless of interests of individual members of the group. Most of the time we want groups to operate that way as we need groups to perform the functions they were created to perform. They are instruments for human ends and to that extent they are like machines. Group bias can be harmful because groups cannot love and yet they exert a tremendous impact on individual members, and they influence virtually all human actions and interactions. Harmful groups tend to remove the transcendentals/Love as the guiding factor for the operations of the cognitional process during interactions between persons. When groups pressure individual group members to adopt the aims or intentional states of the group as their own individual intentional states, the individual is empowered to do both great good and great harm. In such a case the agent intellect uses group aims instead of individual desire and love to guide its operations. If it refuses to let desire and love guide the overall cognitional process of experience, understanding, and judgment, then forms that should be brought into actuality (e.g. haecceity of the Other) cannot be brought into consciousness, and forms that ought not to be brought into consciousness (the mechanically categorized and dehumanized individual) will be brought into the cognitional process and used to interact with others.

What causes the agent intellect to opt for knowledge of the Other without Love? It is primarily due to the fact that the group necessarily opposes the individual agent's idiosyncratic intentions and desires. The group's efficiency and power stem from its ability to partially nullify the individual's idiosyncratic desires along with his core rational faculty and his personhood, his intentional states, and to replace them with the groups' own intentional states. In order to be effective groups must unify its members around group aims. The greater the unity the greater the group effectiveness. Groups can have and do enact intentional states but they cannot love or access the transcendentals. Groups cannot feel the suffering of an individual. Groups, good or bad, are only interested in increasing their numbers, weight, density, and power.[1] They must do so if they are to fulfill their intended functions. They accomplish their aims by preventing dis-unity among members. Groups are interested in persons only insofar as they embody group attributes common to every other member of the group. Unique individual attributes are not seen or valued by the group. There is in every group, even the best groups, an animus against real diversity, intellectuality, and knowledge because real intellectuality can only find expression as creativity in an individual.

Now of course groups are necessary. We could not survive without groups of all kinds. Like machines they are not neutral tools that we can wield without consequences. They have their own purposes, agency, and aims that sometimes coincide with the individuals that compose them but most often do not coincide with individual aims. When groups oppose individual aims that are destructive to persons, groups perform a good and necessary action. But the only way we can ensure groups perform functions that benefit persons is to monitor group actions and effects. We depersonalize individuals when we fail to notice and value their unique attributes and values. We are most likely to do that when we let group aims shape our intellectual apprehension of others. Once a group-level intentional state replaces an individual's intentional state he becomes vulnerable to depersonalization and is therefore more likely to depersonalize others when he interacts with them. When depersonalization becomes a stable part of the individual's identity love can only inform that group-controlled individual's intentional states via suffering (again because only individuals can suffer) or via exit or exclusion from the group.

The most dangerous kind of group is the mob, but the most efficient in promotion of evil is what Oakeshott[2] called the "enterprise group"—a group dedicated to some overarching or universal purpose or enterprise (utopia, money, or power). An enterprise group can often accomplish great things but it can also turn into an ideologically driven machine whose only goal is realization of its universal purpose. Eschatological and utopian groups can be understood as enterprise groups, so it is incumbent upon eschatological personalism to build in safeguards against deformations in group dynamics that lead to dehumanization of members and out-group violence. Enterprise groups often have lofty goals and these goals are considered more important than the individual. It necessarily calls for depersonalization of its individual members as its members are required to sacrifice themselves and to act on behalf of the group purpose rather than individual aims or conscience. When the enterprise group is also highly entitative (as most religious groups are), the group requires submersion and fusion of the individual's identity and intentional states into that of the group identity and intentional states. Thus, depersonalization in the context of highly entitative, "enterprise associations" is the proximate cause of individual evil acts as the group replaces the individual's intentional states with its own. This replacement process prevents the agent intellect from performing its normal task (with respect to person perception) of grasping the unique value inherent in each individual and of bringing the true, the good, and the beautiful into being.

Problems with the theory of evil as nothingness

Locating a major source of evil in groups contrasts to some extent with the traditional position of evil as a privation or nothingness. The position that individual evil originated in a choice for nothingness began of course with Augustine's reflections on evil in the Confessions.[3] I note that Augustine himself realized that a key facilitator of his career in sin was pressure from a group, a particular kind of group, a group where mind is "seduced" and free agency is submerged into group enthusiasms. Aquinas (Articles 48–49 Summa Theologiae) entertains the possibility that evil is introduced into human action when an agent intellect intends one potential form as a target for apprehension and misses it but allows another potential form to come into being or consciousness due to the error. Aquinas argues that both forms are inherently good to the extent that they have being. But it is reasonable to assume that when a form that should not be brought into existence/consciousness is nevertheless brought into existence/consciousness by the agent intellect, it constitutes a potential source for evil. When forms that should not be are nevertheless brought into consciousness by the agent intellect they nevertheless have effects in the real world and these effects are often evil. The operations of the agent intellect work properly and fully only when guided by desire for the true, the good, and the beautiful, i.e. by Love. Love operating through the agent intellect fully apprehends/abstracts/assimilates intelligible species of forms and it can guide the cognitional process into that second phase of its operations, apprehension of value—especially value inherent in the Other. These forms and values are fully brought into consciousness or actualized via Love's cognitional effects. When Love is prevented from operating through the free choice of the agent, then some forms/values that ought to be realized are not realized or not fully realized and other forms that should not be realized are realized. These latter existents can truly be considered monstrous.

Both the agent intellect and Bernard Lonergan's so-called "cognitional process"[4] operate on the intelligible species of forms and bring forms out of a potential state (non-consciousness) into consciousness as images. Lonergan showed that it is the experience of these images that give rise to knowing and to the experience of insight. Thus, imagination is crucial for the cognitional process. Lonergan's treatment of general and group bias is crucial for understanding why some people flee from insight and eschew rational self-reflective consciousness. When insight is prevented due to group bias, apprehension of intelligible forms, or value, of order that should have been cannot be grasped by consciousness. Like Augustine and Aquinas before him, however, Lonergan does not see that something more than mere privation of order happens when evil appears. Not only is disorder introduced as the absence of an order that should have been, but in addition, *things that should not have been also make an appearance and exert effects.* Alternate worlds are accessed that should not have been accessed. This result follows from the logic of the corruption of the cognitional process. When the agent can no longer use his intentional states to fully grasp intelligible species in forms and bring them into consciousness as wholes or unities, the agent intellect does not cease to operate. It cannot do so without annihilating the agent himself. In addition, the group imposes its intentional states on the agent who is then pressured to makes his choices based upon group aims. If those group aims include the transcendentals then all proceeds well, but all too often group aims are narrow and concern aggrandizement of group density and power only. Thus, the agent intellect selects other species and forms that do not reflect the true, the good, and the beautiful but instead reflects group bias.

Like machines, groups are always and primarily interested in increasing their numbers, weight, density, and power. These traditional group aims have been dramatically enhanced in recent years via recruitment of machines in service to group aims. A potent contributor to group bias not considered by Lonergan is the contribution of intelligent machines to enhancing group effectiveness, density, and power. The ubiquity of machines in the social world forces the entire culture to adopt machine logics or technological rationality where utility functions and effectiveness metrics rule rather than idiosyncratic and eccentric individuals. The culture needs these machines and they do a lot of good. We cannot do without them, but we need to control them rather than them controlling us. When the agent intellect or the cognitional process operates under conditions of machine-enabled group power it still attempts to grasp intelligible species and values but it cannot see or grasp persons as wholes or unities or as unique. Instead it grasps persons in terms of group categories or as means to group ends.

Eschatological personalism is suspicious of groups of all kinds. Human beings evolved away from group life when we evolved away from primates and higher apes. Compared with most Old World monkeys, apes and humans evolved low density social networks, low sociality, and strong individualistic feeding and mating patterns.[5] Hunter–gatherer groups of the upper Paleolithic probably never numbered more than about 8–10 bands or about 50 people. Most of these groups engaged in cyclical migrations following the herds of animals they hunted. They were therefore never exposed to very large number of individuals or groups. One would have to travel hundreds of miles to meet other human groups. Mostly patrilocal residence patterns were observed where females would disperse out of the group to marry into a distant group. This sort of residence and mating pattern also militated against formation of large coalitions as females found themselves among strangers after they married. Their religious culture was very likely shamanic. That is unusual individuals were accorded extraordinary respect. Religious visions were assumed to be delivered to individuals via dreams and during lone vision quests to remote areas. Hunters, in particular, spent very long periods of time utterly alone in vast wildernesses where no other human would be seen for weeks, even months on end. Because of the low density population networks these individuals moved within, disease was uncommon though hunting-related injuries were common. Especially successful hunters were accorded great prestige and stood out compared to other members of the band. Attempts by hunters to become spectacular hunters were good for the group but simultaneously encouraged a kind of primitive individualism among these men. In short our hunter–gatherer ancestors were not adapted to large groups of people. While they lived within small groups of generally related individuals there was also space for individuals to thrive as well as great mobility and freedom of movement.

The rise of agriculture encouraged aggregation and settlement of large numbers of people in a single geographic region. The close and unsanitary living conditions of these large population centers encouraged spread of all kinds of diseases. Room for the individual developed to a small extent with the rise of cities with its diverse occupational roles and surplus of goods. Literacy and the increase of knowledge also encouraged individual efforts to stand out from the crowd—though crowds were now a permanent feature of human lifeways.

Since the onset of the industrial age in the modern era the world's population has grown exponentially from 1 billion people in 1800, to an estimated 8–10 billion by the end of this century. Overcrowding into urban centers are major factors in the transmission of physical and psychiatric diseases including diseases with epidemic potential such as acute respiratory infections, meningitis, typhus, cholera, scabies, though it must be admitted that most of these dire effects can be ameliorated if poverty and malnutrition were targeted before the issue of overcrowding. Nevertheless, large numbers of people congregating in a single region create conditions for competition for scarce resources and thus for poverty and overcrowding. Crowding increases the risk of multiple infections because the number of potential transmitters is increased, and the nearness or proximity between disease hosts and potential hosts is increased and then once infected time to recovery may be increased due to repeated exposures to the original and to new infectious agents if the individual remains within the overcrowded group.

Overcrowding also leads to increased potential for pollution. High ambient levels of air pollution have been linked to infant mortality and hospital admissions for cardiac, pulmonary, and cerebral vascular disease. Today 40% of US waters are unfit for drinking, fishing, or swimming. Overcrowding is also leading to deforestation of three-quarters of all forests (which protects what remains of the biodiversity on the planet and contributes along with ocean dynamics to stable weather systems). In addition, 20–50% of global wetlands have been destroyed due to overcrowding. Again, I emphasize that overcrowding is not the only problem. Poverty and injustice create the conditions for overcrowding to potentiate disease transmission and pollution. All three problems, overcrowding, poverty, and injustice need to be tackled all at once. My point here is that large groups of people can increase risk for a multitude of problems for individual persons. In addition to the physical problems crowds create for individuals there are also the psychic or cognitive problems associated with crowd psychology.

Groups and depersonalization

Taking on the moral ideology or aims of a given group can powerfully alter intentional states of members of that group.[6,7] The group does this by altering the sense of agency or Self of the individual. The Self, of course, is a complex, socially constructed but biologically constrained entity. The Self is defined by sense of agency, intentionality, and decision-making processes. The sense of Self as "agent" appears to draw on several psychological and neuropsychological domains such as autobiographical memory, emotional and evaluative systems, self-monitoring, bodily awareness, subjectivity, or perspectivalness in perception. But the core processes most implicated in sense of the acting Self per se are agency, Will, and rationality. These are the core processes that make us individual acting persons and yet these are the very processes that groups seek to alter. When groups alter the sense of Self what generally occurs is some degree of depersonalization.

Depersonalization is the loss of individual intentional states and the concomitant ability to feel normal feelings. It is the loss of self-awareness, autonomy, and self-control, and the transference of basic functions of the Self, such as empathy and intercourse with others, over to a group. In short there is a reduction in self-awareness and an increase in group or social identity. Typically the transfer of Self is to a group that the individual identifies with. It is, to use a technical term, a highly entitative group. The group carries much of the individual's identity such that the individual is comfortable adopting the group's actions as his own. If the group stigmatizes some other out-group as noxious, so too will the individual once de-individuation occurs. If the group acts with a kind of herd mentality, moving with fads or waves of irrational attachments to various salient "ideas", so too will the individual once depersonalization occurs. If the group decides that violent elimination of other groups or of selected individuals is necessary, the individual member of the group will produce rationales to justify the violence, once depersonalization occurs. How then does depersonalization occur?

De-individuation, as distinct from depersonalization, is commonly understood to involve a reduction in self-awareness and a resultant social anonymity such that responsibility for behavioral acts is diffused throughout the group (e.g. Zimbardo, 1969[8]). Unlike, the case of depersonalization, however, de-individuation may not be associated with a concomitant increase in social identity. Instead of a merging of Self with the group the individual who is de-individuated seems to just drift or to become powerless. While both de-individuation and depersonalization harm the individual psychically, depersonalization is fraught with greater potential for evil and that is because depersonalization involves not just a decrease in personal awareness but a replacement of personal identity with a group identity—a merging of the Self with the group. This replacement process fundamentally requires a replacement of the individual's intentional states with the intentions/purposes of the group. Instead of a person we get a group entity, a kind of machine. Now the person functions not in pursuit of his own aims but in pursuit of the group aim. The group calls the shots and the individual loses self-control and personal autonomy as well as his capacity to feel the suffering of others.

The point here is that groups and crowds tend to be inimical to values of personalism and the personalist must therefore be wary of groups and crowds. Most importantly groups and crowds tend to replace the intentional states of the individuals with intentional states of the group and thus the agent intellect's ability to realize instances of the true, the good, and the beautiful is compromised in favor of group bias. The evil that groups produce is not merely parasitic on being. It is something that has density, weight, and reality. The theory of evil as mere privation needs to be supplemented by our new understanding of group effects.

Augustine on evil in the "Confessions"

To understand the extensiveness of the effects of group-supported evils, it will be necessary to dig a little deeper into the origins of the theory of evil as nothingness. We can retain that theory, as some forms of evil are best characterized as parasitic on being, but it is time to supplement that traditional theory with the notion that some forms of evil exist in an intermediate or liminal realm. The realm where we fallen ones live and that evil has density and some form of limited reality that is characteristic of all things in the liminal realm. To see the power and the limitations of the evil as privation position, let's look briefly at its origins and logic.

The Confessions[9] of Saint Augustine of Hippo (354–430) were written when he was in his 40s and sometime after his conversion to orthodox Christianity. He was, at the time, Bishop of Hippo in modern day Algeria. He lived at a time when the Roman Empire was in crisis. In the middle of his life around the year 410, the Goths sacked Rome itself. The sack of Rome led Augustine to write his massive City of God.[10] Twenty years later, as Augustine lay dying, a second Germanic tribe, the Vandals, invaded North Africa and captured Hippo right after Augustine's death. These conquests by the Germanic tribes that took place throughout Augustine's life spelled an end to the 1,000 year old Roman Empire. Augustine very likely was affected by this world-historical change.

During his early adulthood Augustine was a member of the Manichean sect or religion. This was an interesting amalgam of Christianity, dualistic Gnosticism, and old-world Zoroastrianism. The Manichees solved the problem of evil by asserting that God was not evil, but evil was a primordial force opposed to God's will for creation. After his conversion to Christianity (chronicled in the Confessions), Augustine battled two other sets of religious ideas or heresies that nevertheless colored his theory of evil. These heretics were called the Donatists and the Pelagians. The Donatists believed that only sin-less or morally upright priests and bishops could legitimately administer the sacraments. Augustine argued that the grace-imparting efficacy of the sacraments did not depend on the spiritual state of the minister administering the sacrament. The Pelagians on the other hand argued that human beings were not significantly enslaved by sin. Human free will enabled people, by their own concerted efforts, to attain to God without any special intervention from God. The Pelagians also downplayed the need for infant baptism and questioned the whole idea of original sin. Augustine argued that Adam's sin introduced disorder and death into the human race and made it very difficult, but not impossible, for people to use their free will to will the good, the true, and the beautiful.

In the Confessions Augustine presents a sketch of his views concerning the nature, origin, and remedy for evil. The Confessions are composed of 13 books, with the middle book (book VII) most directly concerned with the nature, origin, and remedy for evil. While the first nine books contain a narrative of Augustine's life, they also are littered with philosophical asides and theological speculations. The last four books are more directly philosophical. They address topics that are central to Augustine's theory of evil. These include memory, time, scripture, and the nature of creation and the Church.

Throughout the Confessions, Augustine introduces conceptual paradoxes that are relevant for the questions of God, evil, and salvation. Although God is immutable, He changes everything we mortals are exposed
to. Although we do not have God, we are aware that we do not have Him.
We must therefore in some sense have him—else we would not be aware of
the absence at all. Similarly, in the memory we may be aware that we have
forgotten something but when we find it in memory we know that that was
indeed the thing we had forgotten. So we must have had some knowledge
of the thing in question—else we would never had recognized the thing
when it came back to us out of our memories. Similar paradoxes abound
with respect to our desires. We desire what we do not have. Yet how can
we know that we desire something unless we in some sense already possess
it or know it? We possess the desire in our memory and to that extent we
know a simulacrum of the thing desired. We may be able to explain these
sorts of paradoxes via the predictive processing framework (PPF) we have
been assuming throughout this book as well as some version of Lewisian
possible worlds theory. We both have and do not have something because
we model the possible worlds we desire (the things we do not have) in as
much detail as possible. Then the brain looks for information that does not
match the model and adjusts the model accordingly so that over time it contains or captures essential qualities of the thing we are interested in. Thus,
some piece of the thing desired is captured in the model before the search
for relevant sensory information commences. Similarly, we already know
something that we have forgotten or that we desire because they already
exist in accessible possible worlds and we have some information about
those possible worlds.

In the case of desire the paradox is linked with the nature of evil itself.
Much of the Confessions is given over to Augustine's struggles with sexual
lust and disordered desire or concupiscence. Augustine notes the paradoxical
nature of being unfree and yet free when one is dominated by one's own
lusts. We feel compelled to return to the lust, the theater of our unfreedom—
despite not wanting to do so, and despite having the power to avoid that fate.
We willingly become will—less or depersonalized. We flee from rationality,
awareness, and freedom into ignorance, automatism, and non-being.

This I take is one of the strands of meaning concerning the nature of evil
Augustine pursues in the story of how he (when he was a teenager) and his
friends stole some pears from a neighbor's tree. The crime was without
motivation. He was not hungry, not angry at the neighbor, not bored, and
not attempting to get the fruit for anybody else. He stole the pears simply
out of a perverse desire for disorder and malice. The urge to do the deed,
Augustine argues, came out of nothing and was purely destructive.

> What fruit did I ever reap from those things which I now blush to re-
> member, and especially from that theft in which I found nothing to love
> save the theft itself, wretch that I was? It was nothing, and by the very
> act of committing it I became more wretched still.[11]

In Book VII Augustine develops the theme of the human penchant for nihilistic nothingness. He starts with the assumption that God is good; that His substance is the greatest good. God is Being for Augustine and Being is good. "What need is there to prove at length why that substance which is God cannot be corruptible. If it were it would not be God".[12] All that God has created is also good because it all comes from God's hand. "Evil, therefore, is not a substance; if it were, it would be good"[13] because it would have come from the hand of God. But Augustine does not seem to consider the possibility that goodness is not a substance and that some things can come into the intermediate realm between being and non-being and these things can be construed as evil—at least some of these liminal things will be evil.

"Where then is evil, where does it come from and how does it creep in? What is its root, its seed? Or does it not exist at all?"[14] ...Speaking to God, Augustine says,

> For you evil has no being at all, and this is true not of yourself only, but of everything you have created, since apart from you there is nothing that could burst in and disrupt the order you have imposed on it.[15]

But Augustine fails to consider human beings as God created them: fully autonomous beings who have the power to bring into being some "things". When we collaborate with God the things we bring into being are good, but when we act alone chance rules and some of the things we bring into being are monstrous evil things. If evil is a nothingness, then what is all this evil we all experience and do each day of our lives?

> I inquired then what villainy might be, but I found no substance, only the perversity of a will turned away from you, God the supreme substance, towards the depths—a will that throws away its life within and swells with vanity abroad.[16]

For Augustine, then, the source of evil in the world is a turning away from God, a kind of involution of the will, a perversion of the will, an option for nihilation rather than being, a choosing of lower values on the scale of values/being, rather than higher values. All of this rings true but when we turn away from God there is not mere nothingness as WE are not mere nothingness. God created real beings when he created us. Therefore, we too can bring things from out of the realm of the possible and into the realm of the actual. Trouble is that when we do so we sometimes bring evil into the realm of the actual.

Does Augustine's notion of evil as a perverse willing of nihilation work? His central claim that the turn away from God and toward nihilation was essentially perverse implies that there is no rational reason for evil. Evil is essentially a flight from reason. But if this is correct then individuals cannot be held responsible for their actions as their actions had no rhyme or reason. The choice to opt for irrational nothingness is essentially irrational itself and groundless in Augustine's theory. Aquinas argues that God's essence is equivalent to his existence. He is not Being per se, but pure ACT—a category beyond Being. ACT is not a substance and therefore the opposite of ACT (evil) may be some form of substance. Both Lonergan and Aquinas appear to slip back and forth between treating God as the supreme Being and treating God as beyond Being. Lonergan refers to Being as the object of the unrestricted pure desire to know[17] and the totality of all that is. God is the uncreated light. Lonergan refers to God's goodness as something different from Being which is created. Aquinas refers to God as the only being whose essence is the same as His existence and in this sense He is beyond Being. Yet both Lonergan and Aquinas also treat God as the supreme Being just as Augustine did. A personalist theist would have no difficulty understanding God as both the supreme Being and something beyond Being itself. That is because personhood is both with and beyond time. The characteristics of the personal (unified awareness, agency, freedom, love, and rationality) can characterize creativity itself as well as determinant beings. In any case, Augustine's focus on evil as non-being due to the perversion of the will cannot be the whole story. The will that chooses oblivion still has to be explained.

Augustine himself seems to intuit that this question needs to be answered. In Book II chapter 8 right after the lines I quoted above:

> I inquired then what villainy might be, but I found no substance, only the perversity of a will turned away from you, God the supreme substance, towards the depths—a will that throws away its life within and swells with vanity abroad.[18]

Augustine says:

> And yet, as I recall my state of mind at the time I would not have done it alone. It follows, then, that I also loved the camaraderie with my fellow thieves. So it is not true to say that I loved nothing other than the theft? Ah, but it is true, because that gang mentality too was a nothing.[19]

"...What an exceedingly unfriendly form of friendship that was! It was a seduction of mind hard to understand, which instilled into me a craving to do harm for sport and fun".[20] Here, Augustine traces his penchant for stealing the pears to the seduction of Mind the group imposed on him with respect to doing harm. But surely stealing the pears was not for mere sport and fun as Augustine himself realizes. Stealing the pears was imposed on Augustine (via "seduction of the mind") by the group/gang, and he stole them to increase the power and density (the fusion of wills of its members) of the gang. How did the gang corrupt Augustine's mind and will? To answer this question we need to first get clearer about mind and will and how they interact to produce moral and immoral acts.

Lonergan on cognitional operations

While the discussion of Augustine and Aquinas has shown us how evil results from a corrupted set of intentional states, and that the resultant evil can be thought of as both a privation and a potent force...as both a thing that should have been but was not and a thing that should NOT have been but is... neither Augustine or Aquinas were clear as to why the agent intellect entertains corrupted intentional states in the first place. Here I turn to the arguably personalist philosopher and theologian, Bernard Lonergan (1904–1984 for help.

In his major work *Insight*[21] Lonergan discusses what it means to know. He provides a phenomenology of the process of knowing that involves the process of experiencing, understanding, and judgment. The raw material for knowledge is experience. Experience is derived from the senses. While experiencing is an act of awareness (deriving images from forms) it is not yet understanding or true knowing. The act of understanding delivers true knowing. It sublates the awarenesses achieved in experiencing and enriches them with a grasp of the universals and intelligibles abstracted from the forms encountered in experience. These intelligibles are put into a meaningful order during the process of understanding. But the process of inquiry or knowledge-seeking does not stop there. Once intelligibles are ordered the knower reflects on them and derives their inherent values. Judgment imposes a hierarchy of significances on the intelligibles. It sublates or enriches the order or unity imposed on the intelligibles by the understanding and adds the element of value to them. This three-fold process of knowing eventuates in a sudden grasp of a provisional unity of all the intelligibles the mind is grappling with in a single act of knowing. This is the experience of insight. The knower then knows that he knows and he appreciates what used to be a mere collection of images or objects as instead a unified whole that has meaning and significance. In the process of grasping this new unity the knower realizes that his knowing accomplished this fact and this is self-reflective awareness. This self-reflective awareness of rational knowing that one knows implies that the knowledge is trustworthy and significant. Because being is intelligible, the three-fold process of knowing is also isomorphic with the structure of the real or being itself.[22] Now, in the Thomistic tradition, being is fundamentally composed of form, potency, and act. Experience matches form as it operates on the forms. Understanding matches potency as it brings the forms out of non-being (potentia) and into potency or being. It grasps the unities and laws that underlie forms presented to experience. Understanding is intellectual and gives us a grasp of necessity or law that is Being.[23] Act matches judgment as the judgment presupposes experience and understanding and it yields fact or a decision about what is and what is significant.

Given his analyses of the cognitional process how does Lonergan deal with evil? He largely accepts Aquinas's analysis of evil and notes that since being is pronounced good by God, evil must have no positive reality because evil is the opposite of good. But, as I argued above, this conception of evil is only partially correct. Like Augustine, Lonergan argues that evil finds its roots in irrationality and it results from the breakdown of the cognitional process. It is a flight from insight.

> Just as insight can be desired, so too it can be unwanted. Besides the love of light, there can be a love of darkness...if prepossessions and prejudices notoriously vitiate theoretical investigations, much more easily can elementary passions bias understanding in practical and personal matters.[24]

This darkening of the intellect Lonergan calls "dramatic bias",[25] and it has ripple effects on the individual's whole psychology. It splits his psychology and orients him inwardly such that he develops a kind of "scotosis" that prevents him from seeing the light. He actively discounts facts that could enlighten his understanding and lead him to insight. He finds it more difficult to discern what is truly good. If the intellect does not know what is truly good, the will is not able to direct action appropriately and so disorder ensues and this disorder ripples into relationships with others. Dramatic bias becomes habitual such that information that conflicts with the bias is screened out and information consistent with the bias is let in. Dramatic bias, when habitual becomes individual bias[26] and individual bias, when rampant among the people becomes group bias[27] and when many or most groups in a culture are biased we get general bias.[28] Group bias is similar to dramatic/individual bias, but its intent is to preserve and promote the interests of a dominant group, at the expense of individuals and other groups. General bias erroneously values commonsense knowledge as ultimate knowledge and eschews true theoretical knowledge. It too, then, is ultimately a flight from rational self-consciousness.

If these various forms of anti-intellectual bias are the sources of evil, what causes bias in the first place? What causes a turn toward darkness of the intellect? Yes, the effort of inquiry is hard but surely it is not so hard as to engender flight from inquiry and love of darkness? It is difficult to pinpoint exactly what Lonergan considered to be the source of bias as his discussions were prolix and complex. Nevertheless, at one point[29] he appears to argue that the human community inherently generates tension due to conflicts between human individuality, inter-subjectivity, and cultural and social order. Although he never, so far as I can see, says directly that groups are what create bias I read his reflections on the dialectic of community tensions to suggest just that. Basically, the tensions arising from the need to live in groups create an opening for evil. Humans have to cooperate with one another in order to create social order but that cooperation is difficult due to diverse interests. Humans create groups in order to solve the problem of cooperation, but the groups they create can have deleterious or beneficent effects or both. Lonergan himself discussed the deleterious effects of groups in his discussion of general and group bias. His description of cultural or general bias reduces in my opinion to group bias that has no inherent corrective principal (due for example to competition of ideas across groups as discussed by Lonergan). Thus, my reading of Lonergan suggests to me that groups are a potent source of bias and evil. We nevertheless need to create groups in order to survive. The task is to work out how to create groups that avoid bias and that promote human flourishing rather than evil.

Cosmopolis

The solution, which in *Insight* is named "cosmopolis", essentially takes the scientific or scholarly community and recommends it as a model for group living. Scientists have developed systematic methods to counteract bias. They constitute an international community that cooperates across boundaries and steadily cumulates knowledge over time for the benefit of all. They exemplify the unrestricted desire to know.

While it is true that science has procedures that systematically correct for bias, Lonergan may be a bit too laudatory here with respect to science. There are many instances of scientists blindly following the herd and intellectual fashions and fads. To the extent that scientists have allied with technical rationality they tend too to be compromised by their infatuation with machines. So while we can and should adopt the scientific paradigm as our model for Cosmopolis, we need a more nuanced understanding of the forms of cooperative or group behavior most conducive to free inquiry and the unrestricted desire to know.

It can be argued there are two major forms of groups: "civil" and "enterprise" associations.[30,31] In civil associations individuals rule, under some agreed upon law or contract. In enterprise associations managers rule and individuals exist for the purpose of the enterprise whatever it is. Of course, there is a place for both types of groups and both types of groups can harm people in various ways but enterprise associations are by far more dangerous in terms of potential for evil. It should now be clear why that is the case: enterprise associations are highly entitative groups that demand surrender of individual aims and identities so that the group purpose can be accomplished. Every human group varies in the extent to which it is civil or enterprise. Religions and political entities tend to be enterprise associations and thus fraught with high potential for evil. Religions in particular exhibit both tendencies. On the one hand most religions encourage personal growth and transformation as well as self-control and individual autonomy.

On the other hand many religions also emphasize ethnic and group allegiances that tend to demand a sacrifice of personal autonomy. In short, the story is complex but it seems safe to say the depersonalization in the context of highly entitative, "enterprise associations" carries the greatest potential for evil. Once the group's intentional states take over the individual's intentional apparatus the agent intellect of that individual no longer is guided by his or her unrestricted desire to know or the transcendentals. Therefore, the agent intellect operates in a biased manner and does not bring into being those forms which should be brought into being when aiming at the true, the good, and the beautiful. Instead criteria for choosing forms are decided by group aims and the group almost always aims at power, profit, and the destruction of individuals. Even the best of groups are biased against Love so how can we construct groups that promote love and intellectual inquiry?

In chapter 20 of *Insight*, Lonergan discusses 31 points that speak to a response to evil. As mentioned above his fundamental recommendation is to construct the Cosmopolis along the lines of the scientific community. But in chapter 20 he also suggests that something more is needed: a grace-filled community. Lonergan points out that group dynamics, the inherent tensions within community, give rise to civilizational effects. Cultures are always simultaneously progressing toward liberty, declining away from inquiry or seeking redemption from decline. Lonergan argues that God has foreseen (since there are no divine afterthoughts) the need for redemption and already provided for it in the existing world order. The solution to group induced evil must transcend groups. There will be required "new conjugate thought forms" or habits of inquiry. There will be a need to cooperate with God's solution to the problem of groups and this cooperation will depend on cultivation of the supernatural virtues: faith, hope, and charity—virtues inimical to group think. Ultimately, Cosmopolis will need to give way to the building up of the Kingdom of God as envisioned in the eschatological traditions of the Church.

To summarize the long argument presented in this chapter: only a free agent can love (there is no such thing as forced love) and therein lies the dignity of the free agent. When actions are performed with Love, they are most voluntary and most free. If the agent intellect cognizes a thing or person with the eyes of Love, then it most perfectly apprehends or appropriates its form or intelligible species—it most perfectly brings it from potentiality into actuality, into Being. Love allows one to know a thing or person most perfectly, and it allows me to know that I am knowing (bringing a form from potentiality into actuality) because Love involves contact or even a union of the thing known and the knower. Love, therefore, is also the basis of insight and self-reflective, rational consciousness. To know is to bring forms into being from potentiality, and when love guides this intellectual process the forms brought into being are more fully actualized; their unity is more firmly grasped in a moment of insight and more deeply assimilated into the rational consciousness of the free agent. What allows this love-driven intellectual process to occur is the ethical and spiritual state of the agent/knower. The greater the self-reflective capacity of the knower, the greater his capacity to love, and to achieve insight into the true, the good, and the beautiful. When this intellectual process occurs without love, the intelligibility of the form (its truth, goodness, and beauty) is obscured, and thus, it cannot be grasped or fully assimilated into the agent's knowing. Its full coming into being is denied and this allows an opening for evil. Group bias is a significant source of evil as it compromises the free and voluntary status of the agent's cognitional processes. Group bias depersonalizes the agent and replaces his desires and cognitional processes with its own desires. The biased group therefore makes the agent less capable of higher forms of cognition based on Love. When group bias operates apprehension/appropriation of form is distorted in such a way as to bring into actuality only those aspects of form congenial to the group bias, thus reinforcing bias and contributing to group structures that ultimately impact long-term historical cycles that reinforce propensity to sin (as described by Lonergan).

The idea that there are forms that are inherently monstrous and evil and that should not see the light of day or existence seems logical to me. These forms need not be thought of as a part of the divine substance or created by God. The source of the potential pool of forms could have derived from the free activities of the myriad creatures created by God. They are a realm of the totality that is not being, not substance but potential being. They are intermediate between nothingness and being and many orthodox authors have pointed to this realm as a potential source of evil in addition to the realm of nothingness. Being precise about the sources of evil helps us in the long run to more effectively combat our own evil inclinations and thus I think that inquiry into evil is helpful as it leads to hope for its final defeat.

Notes

1 Canetti, Elias. *Crowds and power.* New York: Macmillan, 1962.
2 Oakeshott, Michael. *On human conduct.* London: Clarendon Press, 1991.
3 Augustine, Saint. *The confessions.* R.S. Pine-Coffin trans. London: Penguin Classics; New Impression edition November 30, 1961.
4 Lonergan, B. *Insight: A study of human understanding.* Toronto: University of Toronto Press, Scholarly Publishing Division; 5th edition V. 3 of Collected Works, 1992.
5 Maryanski, Alexandra, and Jonathan H. Turner. *The social cage: Human nature and the evolution of society.* Stanford: Stanford University Press, 1992.
6 Haney, Craig, Curtis Banks, and Philip Zimbardo. "Interpersonal dynamics in a simulated prison." *International Journal of Criminology and Penology* 1 (1973): 69–97.
7 Zimbardo, Philip. *The Lucifer effect: Understanding how good people turn evil.* New York: Random House, 2007.
8 Zimbardo, Philip G. "The human choice: Individuation, reason, and order versus deindividuation, impulse, and chaos." In Arnold, W.J. and Devine, D., Eds., *Nebraska symposium on motivation.* Lincoln: University of Nebraska Press, 1969.

9 Augustine, Saint. *The confessions*. R.S. Pine-Coffin, trans. London: Penguin Classics; New Impression edition 1961.
10 Augustine, Saint. "The city of god, trans." *Markus Dods*. New York, NY: Modern Library,1950.
11 Confessions Book II 16. p. 47.
12 Confessions Book VII 6. p. 167.
13 Confessions Book VII 18. p. 182.
14 Confessions Book VII 7. p. 168.
15 Confessions, Book VII 19. p. 182.
16 Confessions, Book VII 22. p. 185.
17 Lonergan, Bernard. *Insight: A study of human understanding* (vol. 3). Toronto: University of Toronto Press, 1992, p. 372 and following.
18 Confessions, Book II 8. p. 47.
19 Confessions, Book II 8. p. 47.
20 Confessions, Book II 9. p. 49.
21 Lonergan, Bernard. *Insight: A study of human understanding* (Collected Works of Bernard Lonergan, vol. 3). Toronto: University of Toronto Press, 1957.
22 Lonergan, Bernard J. F., Elizabeth A. Morelli, and Mark D. Morelli. *Understanding and being: An introduction and companion to Insight: The Halifax lectures* (vol. 5). Lewiston: Edwin Mellen Press, 1980.
23 Lonergan, 1980, p. 391.
24 Lonergan, 1957, p. 214.
25 Lonergan, 1957, p. 214.
26 Lonergan, 1957, pp. 244–247.
27 Lonergan, 1957, pp. 247–250.
28 Lonergan, 1957, pp. 250–257.
29 Lonergan, 1957, p. 243 and following.
30 Oakeshott, Michael. *A place of learning*. Colorado Springs: Research Committee, Colorado College, 1975.
31 Oakeshott, Michael. *On human conduct*. London: Clarendon Press, 1991.

8 Conclusions

In this book, I have tried to sketch the broad outlines of a new personalism, an eschatologically informed personalism. I felt it necessary to do so because I believe that we are moving into a new period of history characterized by massive disruptions in human consciousness including the development of a whole new relationship with the machines we produce. All of the previous proposals for what constitutes the imago Dei in human persons (reason, intelligence, consciousness, etc.) cannot withstand the challenge of the rise of intelligent machines in this new period of history. These machines already exhibit all of the characteristics that have been previously supposed to reflect the imago Dei: rationality, creativity, emotions, mind-reading abilities, calculating abilities, and consciousness itself.

At the heart of the eschatological personalism on offer here is the agent intellect which is subjectively experienced as a form of imaginative care and inquiry. When it operates at the intellectual level it abstracts qualities and universals from the intelligible forms of things it grasps and thus cumulates knowledge about the world. When it is operating emotionally, it adds (instead of abstracts) qualities to the intelligible forms it grasps (concerning things and persons in the world), and this is experienced subjectively as a form of care or love, that is, reverence and care for the haecceity, the unique thisness that is the thing or beloved. The agent intellect can also bring new possibilities into existence. It selects from an infinity of possible worlds and then actualizes its selection. When the agent intellect utilizes the transcendentals to guide its choices, it brings into existence worlds, ideas, or things that enhance the well-being of persons. When it does not use the transcendentals to make choices it brings into existence all manner of good AND bad things.

The idea of the agent intellect, of course, is rooted in the Aristotelian and Thomistic philosophical traditions. The agent intellect is experienced as that activity within us that is rational, imaginative, and oriented toward realization of the transcendentals. It operates to discern those transcendentals in anything it interacts with or brings to life. It brings possible worlds or intelligible forms into Being. It then either adds an indefinite number of qualities to the form it actualizes, or it abstracts such qualities away from a form previously actualized. In the former case the agent intellect discovers the haecceity of the thing, while in the latter, it discovers the universal qualities and principles associated with the form. The abstractive function of the agent intellect tends to operate under slow, focused-effortful, and waking conditions, while the additive function tends to operate quickly and under quasi-automatic dream-like, imaginative conditions.

Because the agent intellect operates on matter or sensory data and not the other way around it is superior to sensible things or matter. Its immediate mental products are what we experience as images. Images allow us to operate on matter and transcend sensory information. Matter does not affect the agent intellect as there is nothing in it that is potential or that needs to be actualized or changed. Instead it is the maker and the actuating principle of matter or existents insofar as it brings possibles into existence. It is all actuality; it manifests no potentiality because it is completely actual; it has no parts and is therefore metaphysically simple and non-instantiable. It cannot be assimilated to anything else in the universe. It is indestructible and immortal. It never tires from activity. Its intellectual activity never ceases. It can reflect on itself but is characterized chiefly by an excess or overflowing giving of itself to intelligible forms which it actualizes and other persons that it loves. This unceasing intellectual activity is felt as a kind of background unity or awareness, a fount of life with intellectual content in consciousness. Since the agent intellect is superior to things and matter it can imaginatively range over the whole of the individual's life and extract meaning from the past, current, and future. It is therefore the source of meaning creation and interpretative activity. Because the agent intellect is at the core of personhood, it constitutes the metaphysical basis of the claim that persons are ultimate and the key to all reality. *A person therefore is a being who can use his free intelligent creative activity as embodied by the agent—intellect to know and love other persons and bring new things and worlds into being from out of the realm of possibility.*

From the Christian perspective, I would argue that persons are metaphysically ultimate and ethically ultimate. They are free agents characterized by unity of experience, autarchy as an existential stance, and love as an eschatological attitude. Autarchy is the effort at self-government and constitutes the basis of the social ethics of eschatological personalism.

Eschatology refers to ultimate and last things such as purpose, freedom, and the final destiny of the individual, humankind, history, and the cosmos. With regard to the self and personhood, an eschatological personalism asserts that the essence of the self can only be grasped as the person's whole history and ultimate end and purpose. From the religious perspective, and particularly Christian, that ultimate fulfillment cannot be known fully until the World's End but will involve some sort of friendship with God. Until the eschaton or End the person must be granted an autarchy or self-rule given that his destiny is supposed to involve a "friendship" with God. According to the Bible, God wants friends, not servants (John, 15:15). Self-rule involves the ability to delay immediate gratification of impulses, and an ability to engage in sustained future-oriented thinking. Although the ultimate end cannot be known in full, an essential element of that End, based upon a religious interpretation, must involve a free collaboration between the individual and God, where the individual ultimately is conceived as a resurrected or transfigured body-mind whole, as well as the building-up of a "beloved community" of all peoples. The individual needs to be free to choose such a possible collaboration or to refuse it. The individual needs to be able to rule over his self and accept responsibility for his free actions and choices to make such a collaboration a real prospect. The end, purpose, destiny, and essence of the person lie in that free collaboration of the self with God; it is a work of two free and sovereign wills. Autarchy, therefore, is the essence of eschatological personalism.

Privacy and solitude are required to contemplate the transcendentals and to build real community. Solitude refers to the spiritual heart of the person, the "place" where no-one, not even God, can gain entry without the consent of the person him or herself. The heart animates the agent intellect, constitutes the metaphysical basis of claims to privacy and sets political limits on state intrusion into personal life.

Eschatological personalism points to new conceptions of the origins of evil in human behavior. When a man forfeits his calling to act as a free agent, to use his agent intellect/intelligence to choose wisely then he also to some extent forfeits his personality and integrity. Depersonalization is associated with distortions in agent intellect activity. Most often these distortions are due to the person's interactions with groups or machines. The Marxist conception of "alienation" from self and others applies here. Once the person consents to group guidance the group can functionally take over control of the person's choices and actions. If the group does not use the transcendentals to guide its functions then that group may obscure the imaginative creativity of the agent intellect within that person and his integrity will be impaired. Then the agent intellect will bring into being worlds, things and ideas that may not enhance the well-being of persons. Sometimes things that should not be brought into being will be brought into Being, when the agent intellect is coerced by the corrupted group. These ideas, possible worlds, acts, or things can be considered a source of evil. This kind of evil is not a mere nothingness or absence of good. It is a positive malignity.

Eschatological personalism entails a different sense of time, a different temporal experience than the standard experience, and this fact carries interesting consequences for the shape and feel of personality for the eschatological personalist. In fact, the eschatological personalist freely navigates between two different temporalities and timelines: one characterized by necessity and futility and the other characterized by freedom and hope. The sense of living as a pilgrim in the current age on the way to the blessed Kingdom of the coming age comes right out of the entire eschatological tradition from Zoroaster right up to the early Christian New Testament texts.

Eschatological personalism reinvigorates the old Christian practice of reverencing dreams and visions as a source of data for doctrine, interpretation, and practical life but tempers enthusiasm for these sources via traditional sources of authority in the ecclesial life. It is oriented daily to the building up of the Kingdom of God but seeks to avoid the twin pitfalls of over-valuing the transcendent at the expense of the mundane, the future versus the now or immanentizing the eschaton (believing that we can build the Kingdom without God) versus eschatologizing the immanent (investing the given with a transcendence it does not have). Similarly, eschatological personalism avoids the twin pitfalls of utterly devaluing my present self in favor of some future ideal self versus over-valuing my present self versus the ideal future self. How does the eschatological personalist maintain his balance between all of these extremes?

He adopts as a rule of autarchy Przywara's *analogia entis* wherein the human governs himself but participates in God's divine life. Such a perspective also seeks to blend the religious and scientific points of view. From the religious perspective, the individual can never match the divine life fully of course. Participation is real but strictly limited. No matter what degree of similarity to God a person theoretically attains, there will always be an infinitely larger dis-similarity. This "similarity in difference" relationship a person perceives to have with God, furthermore, is dynamic and always changing. Psychologically, cognitively, and spiritually, a person can get better and better at becoming "like God" but will never reach an end to that process. The similarity within an ever greater dis-similarity captures the right sort of balance between human and God such that there is no danger of ultimate dissolution of the individual into the whole. Nor is there the opposite danger of experiencing no connection at all to the divine. Instead the connection is perceived to be real and capable of intensifying to an infinite degree.

When the *analogia entis* is applied to the political realm we can avoid immanentizing the eschaton (over-valuing the divine) AND avoid the opposite danger of over-valuing current political arrangements by aiming at immanentizing some of the eschaton but not all of it. That strategy sees the value of the ideal but does not over-value it and similarly it sees the value of the current arrangement but does not over-value it either. The same principle applies to balancing between my current versus ideal selves and between the two warring temporalities at the heart of eschatological personalism. We do not entirely de-value the current age. We see within it the seeds of the coming blessed age and we seek to realize these seeds. We nevertheless anchor ourselves in the coming age such that we are really just pilgrims passing through the current age. We like some of what we see and we culti-vate those things, but the deeper vision is that the entire age is corrupt and subjected to futility. Eschatological personalism argues that our true home lies ahead in what is coming—a revelation of the personal.

Index

Note: **Bold** page numbers refer to tables and page numbers followed by "n" denote endnotes.

184   *Index*

Made in the USA
Middletown, DE
17 January 2023

22293301R00113